Learn to Test, Test to Learn

Learn to Test, Test to Learn

The History of the Empire Test Pilots' School

John Rawlings and Hilary Sedgwick

Airlife
England

First published in the UK in 1991
by Airlife Publishing Ltd.

British Library Cataloguing in Publication Data
Rawlings, John D. R. (John Dunstan Richard) *1925–*
  Learn to test, test to learn
    1. Flying (Aircraft), history. Empire Test Pilots' School
  I. Title II. Sedgwick, Hilary
  629.13252

ISBN 1 85310 080 3

Printed in England by Livesey Ltd., Shrewsbury.

Airlife Publishing Ltd.

101 Longden Road, Shrewsbury SY3 9EB, England.

Contents

Photograph credits
The photographs used in this book are from the author's collection. Jacket photograph © British Crown copyright 1982/MOD reproduced with the permission of the Controller of Her Britannic Majesty's Stationery Office.

Introduction

The second half of this century has seen the emergence of the aircraft as a commonplace vehicle, making air travel part of everyday life, air arms a leading force and the variety of uses for the aeroplane throughout the world multiplying rapidly. One of the key factors in this rapid development has been the contribution made by research and development flying, both by the manufacturers and by Governments. It was to put such flying on a sound footing in the United Kingdom that the subject of this book was formed in 1943 and the Empire Test Pilots' School (such is its quaintly old-fashioned title) has been in the forefront of such key flying ever since.

However, little is known of the Research and Development world of aviation, partly because so much of it has to be shrouded in both military and commercial secrecy and the test flying fraternity still tends to be something of a private world of its own within aviation. Within that world ETPS, as it is known universally, has a record second to none and a high reputation and so as the School now approaches its own half-century we, who have both had our involvement in the test flying world in different ways, have set out to put on record something of the story of this leading organisation within British aviation. In so doing we have had great co-operation from the School itself and by a host of previous members of staff and students, many of whom have told their stories to Hilary and given their permission to be quoted in the book. Without this the book would have been dull, relating of facts alone, but it is our hope that it will not only bring to a greater audience the important and proud role that ETPS has played and still plays today but also give some insight into the varied people who play such a vital role and the task that they have to perform.

Our task would have been impossible but for the kind co-operation of the Ministry of Defence (Procurement Executive), the staff and graduates of the School and, in particular, the following: (rank titles have been omitted as these change from time to time) P. P. C. Barthropp, M. C. Brooke, D. L. Bywater, A. Canetto, A. M. Christie, R. Clear, K. Crawford, A. W. Debuse, I. L. Gonsal, P. Habert, R. S. Hargreaves, J. G. Harrison, R. E. Havercroft, A. J. Hawkes, R. C. Hoewing, M. Hope, V. C. Lockwood, W. L. M. Mayer, G. Maclaren Humphries, C. G. B. McLure, H. A. Merriman, H. J. Nelson, J. H. Orrell, H. P. Powell, J. A. Robinson, J. Rochfort, P. A. Sedgwick, V. Shaw, G. P. L. Shea-Simonds, L. S. Snaith, R. J. Spiers, R. A. Watts, A. Wood, S. Wroath.

John Rawlings
Hilary Sedgwick

CHAPTER 1
Why and How

The designation 'Test Pilot' has always been an emotive one — conjuring up in most people's minds an almost super-human aviator, an image furthered by the popular press and the film industries of the 1930s and '40s, an image which has been a long time a-dying because, for most, the test pilot is a remote figure never to be encountered in daily life. In fact it is an appellation which covers a wide range of tasks from the routine test pilot at a Maintenance Unit, whose job is to check out standard aircraft after they have been in for major servicing or for routine modifications, right through to the firm's Chief Test Pilot who takes to the air for the first time with an advanced design at the very frontier of aerospace knowledge, nowadays a task which takes him into space as well as through the earth's atmosphere. The world of the test fraternity is a surprisingly small one and there are very many persons engaged in the aviation industry itself who have little or no knowledge of the Research and Development field and what it involves.

Like so many other aspects of aviation, when it all began eighty years ago there were no rules or manuals as to how to fly, let alone test aircraft and the brothers Wright began as the first test pilots, testing themselves as much as the 'Flyer'. And for the first ten years of aviation it was just like that; Man was so intent on getting into the air and down again successfully that few attempts were made at systematic analysis of flying or of the machines used, and what was done was largely on a subjective basis. In Britain it was 1915 before concerted attempts were made to set up test establishments for flying research and two such appeared before the end of 1916. The first of these took place at Upavon where the Central Flying School existed; here an Experimental Flight was set up in the summer of 1915 and staffed with pilots returned from operational flying on the Western Front. This Flight was largely concerned with assessing the qualities of new prototypes and their suitability for operational flying, together with armament development, broadly the task carried on by the A&AEE at Boscombe Down today. Then in 1916 the Royal Aircraft Factory at Farnborough became the Royal Aircraft Establishment and was given terms of reference to carry out basic research into all aspects of aviation, a task it has carried on ever since.

At Farnborough the flying was carried out both by Service and civilian pilots, many of whom were principally scientists or designers, flying the aircraft as a logical outcome of the actual research or designing work. One such principal test pilot was the designer Geoffrey de Havilland. Within a year, the Experimental Flight at the CFS had split up, the Armament Experimental Flight going to Orfordness and the Experimental Aircraft Flight to Martlesham Heath and in 1917 the two combined at Martlesham to become, eventually, the Aeroplane and Armament Experimental Establishment (A&AEE). The third such testing establishment was formed at nearby Felixstowe on 1 April 1924 as the Marine Aircraft Experimental Establishment (MAEE).

At these three Establishments test flying was carried out by Service pilots in the 1920s and the leisurely pace at which testing took place ensured that the limited techniques required were easily passed on from team to team. Almost all these pilots were men who had had flying experience in operational squadrons and whose flying ability had been assessed as 'Above Average'.

Alongside the service pilots, private aircraft constructors also employed test pilots to fly their new prototypes. It is unfair to say that they were a 'motley crew' but certainly in World War 1 and the 1920s they were a most diverse body of gallant aviators united by one common skill — the ability to fly difficult aeroplanes and return normally in one piece. Amongst them were giants whose scientific knowledge enabled them to analyse just what was happening to their aeroplane and return with a coherent assessment for the designer on the ground; then there were the designers themselves, such as Barnwell of Bristol, who did their own test-flying in the early days; and finally there were those who were employed because of the dash and verve of their flying skills rather than their scientific knowledge, for such a flair for flying was paramount in selling an aircraft to prospective purchasers. Many a mediocre aircraft could be made to look excellent by the way it was flown on demonstration.

For the first two and a half decades of practical flying this lack of conformity in test pilot skills and abilities mattered little for the advance in aircraft design over the period had moved but slowly — the Hawker Hart of the early 1930s was basically a BE2c of 1915 with a bigger engine, better controls, more sensible crew arrangement, able to fly somewhat faster and carry more bombs; the actual overall aircraft design was the same basic configuration. The test flying of the 1920s and early '30s, whilst certainly more dangerous than it is

today, was a much simpler affair, largely confined to aircraft handling qualities of a fairly basic airframe within limited performance parameters. But during the 1930s the whole picture changed for, with new stressed-skin monoplanes with retractable undercarriages, flaps, variable-pitch propellers and a much higher performance, a great increase in test flying came about and the performance envelopes of the aircraft were much greater. This necessitated a greater standardisation in test procedures and a greater knowledge of the whole field of aviation. The test flying scene was no longer (if it ever really had been) a place for the brilliant amateur.

On the outbreak of World War 2 the two East Coast research establishments moved, the A&AEE to Boscombe Down and the MAEE to Helensburgh on the Clyde. In both these places, and at Farnborough, the research task mushroomed at a tremendous rate so that by the mid-war years one could look over Laffan's Plain from the Aldershot Golf Course and count over a hundred test aircraft on Farnborough's field and, if one could get near Boscombe Down, the number would be even greater. Still the supply of test flying staff came from the Services, men on a posting of around two years at the most, many of whom had been posted to test flying from operational flying as a rest. Thus they came with little idea of the job and even less relish for it. After a life of day-to-day operations the tedious, patient work of test flying, requiring facing up to real dangers in a cool, calculating foreknowledge rather than in the excited heat of battle, was not a life that appealed to very many of them. There were exceptions, like Roland Beamont who came from his Typhoons and Tempests to be one of Britain's outstanding experimental test pilots, but for every man who took to this rather exacting environment there were many who did not. As a result, there was a great variation in the quality of the test results obtained both at the establishments and in the aircraft factories and in 1943 something was done to remedy this situation and bring some standardisation into the system. That something was the Empire Test Pilots School.

As far as can be found out the School was the brainchild of Air Marshal Sir Ralph Sorley ('Eight-Gun Sorley', the man who in the thirties had insisted that the then-new Hurricanes and Spitfires were fitted with eight machine-guns each and thus made a material contribution to the winning of the Battle of Britain). He was a Controller of Research and Development in 1943 and, concerned by the rising number of fatal accidents in test flying together with the lack of standardisation of the flying techniques, set in motion the establishment of a Test Pilots Training Flight at Boscombe Down. Its aims, as set out by Sorley, were:

(a) to improve the breed of test pilots and thereby to ensure a high and consistent standard by which aircraft may be judged;
(b) by being first in the field with a course of irreproachable character and high repute to raise the National prestige of the Empire in the aviation world.

Boscombe Down was chosen as the natural place to begin such an enterprise as it was the seat of the biggest volume of test flying in the country and the locale on Salisbury Plain gave plenty of access for flying uninhibited by operational necessities.

Here was another first for British aviation. No other country had looked as far ahead as this and, with the possible exception of Germany, no other country had already established a school specifically for the standard teaching of test flying techniques in the air. It started as one of the series of 'Empire' schools in the RAF (Empire Central Flying School, Empire Air Navigation School, Empire Air Armament School, Empire Radio School, etc) which were named thus because they were not only staffed by airmen from all over the Empire but were for personnel from all the Imperial Air Forces. The Empire Test Pilots School took this name and is the last of the series still to carry this name, perpetuating on behalf of the RAF one of its wartime traditions. The School was ahead of the world when it was formed and it likes to feel that it is still there today in this highly specialised field.

CHAPTER 2
Boscombe Beginnings

Having decided that there should be a school for test pilots and having obtained all the necessary authorisation the whole task came down from Sorley's office to Boscombe Down to implement. To say that this additional task was not welcome would have had some truth in it for in 1943 the A&AEE was at the height of its wartime experimental task. With approximately 150 experimental aircraft dispersed over its rolling hills, all involved in urgent development programmes, and with a worryingly mounting loss rate amongst its test crews, the Commandant, Air Commodore D'Arcy Greig, had more than enough to cope with, let alone establishing a teaching empire on a Research and Development airfield.

His initial move was to appoint two men to form what was then known as the Test Pilots Training Flight. Wing Commander C. V. Slee, MVO, AFC, a test pilot of no little experience who had recently been at Boscombe Down, was posted in again to become the Officer Commanding, and to set up the flying side, whilst the ground instructional side was given to G. Maclaren Humphreys, a civilian technical officer at A&AEE, to organise as Chief Technical Instructor. Let him take up the story.

'I was second in charge of the Bomber Testing Section at Boscombe Down when I was asked whether I would take on the job of Technical Instructor to the Test Pilots Training Flight. After I had finished my degree at university I had qualified as a teacher and took an education diploma which I never used until I reached ETPS. Now whether this had any bearing on my selection I don't know, but I know I was the only one around the place with a teaching diploma. I thought to myself — this is an impossible task, starting from scratch, with nothing to go on at all.

'I was given a broad outline in that I was to seek help from specialists at Farnborough, the firms if need be, and they also wanted to include things like liaison and visits to the firms. Beyond that it was left entirely to me; I was to draw up a syllabus covering a period of nine months; two months to be taken up with visiting firms and Farnborough. It worked out at about seven months on a daily syllabus basis, covering broadly the things as we taught them — performance testing and testing for handling and stability control. I was told that this was an experimental period and it would be decided after twelve months whether they were going to continue with it or not.'

It speaks volumes for Maclaren Humphreys' foresight and ability that the syllabus he prepared for the original course has been the foundation on which all subsequent syllabi have been built.

As it happened, Wing Commander Slee never actually became part of the setup. Before the organisation really started he was called to the Establishment itself to do clearance trials on a special York which was to be assigned to the King's Flight and this posting took him off three weeks before the School started to the King's Flight itself from which he did not return to Boscombe Down. So D'Arcy Greig had to look around quickly for another senior test pilot to take up the task. He went to the Squadron Commander of 'A' Squadron, the fighter 'empire' at Boscombe, Squadron Leader S. Wroath. This is what happened, in his words.

'My first indication that there was going to be a test pilots' school at Boscombe Down was when the Officer Commanding, Air Commodore D'Arcy Greig, met me on the tarmac and told me about it and suggested that I might like to be the Commandant. At that time I was the Squadron Commander of 'A' Squadron and very happy at it. So I was rather loath to leave it and go across and run some school which didn't seem to have any future in it at all. D'Arcy Greig suggested I might like to have the school; I said that I agreed with the sentiments of the whole thing but I was not going to volunteer for the job. However, if he pushed me into it

then I would do it. So he said the job was mine and that I would get an extra rank out of it (Squadron Leader to Wing Commander). That was how it all started, nothing more nor less than that; in fact, it never even appeared on Station Orders or anything.'

A student on the first course said of Sammy Wroath:

'He was the ideal chap because he was known to all of us very well as a Service test pilot of tremendous practical experience. His approach to the whole business was completely down to earth and his was exactly the right personality, having the ability to get on well with everybody and to steer the whole thing along the right way. To this you could add the tremendous advantage of being able to bribe or blackmail all the Flight Commanders to lend us aeroplanes.'

Between them Sammy Wroath and Maclaren Humphreys acquired a Nissen Hut over the opposite side of the airfield (near where the present helicopter squad-

The embryo Test Pilots' School began in these Nissen huts out in the middle of Boscombe Down airfield in the summer of 1943.

ron is located). This empire soon expanded into three other Nissen Huts, two wooden huts and a wash house, as seen in the accompanying photographs. The next important task was to acquire some aeroplanes for the students to work on. Although there were over 100 aircraft at Boscombe most of these were allocated to test or development programmes and could not be spared; in fact many of them were specially instrumented for the tasks in hand. With the course starting in June, the first aircraft arrived on 26 May; this was *L9520,* a very early Halifax I which had spent most of its life with Dowty, the undercarriage firm, where it was used to become the prototype Mark V with a new Dowty undercarriage. This undercarriage caused it to crash in 1942; it was rebuilt and came to the embryo Test Training Flight but it did not survive the end of the first course, being relegated to a ground instructional airframe in August 1943. But for two months it served as the School's first aircraft. It was followed three days later by a Master III, *W8537,* which had been languishing at No 1 Coastal Artillery Co-operation Unit, and on 3 June a Hurricane I, *L2006,* which was already part of A&AEE. With this trio of widely differing aircraft the Test Flying Training Flight was in business.

The first course came from the RAF, plus two naval officers. It began with eighteen men but five had to drop out because of inadequate academic abilities. The whole enterprise was by way of an experiment and even the arrival of the students was drawn out over a period of two weeks after the course started depending on their replacements arriving on their home units. Typical of those on the first course was Squadron Leader Hedley Hazelden, DFC. He had joined the RAF in 1939 through the RAFVR and began operations as a bomber pilot with 44 Squadron at Waddington on Hampdens. He continued in Bomber Command for three

years, flying Manchesters and Lancasters and collecting his DFC before instructing at a Wellington OTU for a year and then coming to Boscombe Down. After graduating he went to the Heavy Aircraft Test Squadron at A&AEE, following this with commanding the Civil Aircraft Test Section after the war. He then left the Service and joined Handley Page in 1947, almost immediately becoming their Chief Test Pilot for the next two decades.

The Fleet gradually built up during the run of the course which had begun on 10 June 1943 — a Beaufort II, Hurricane II, Proctor and Oxford arriving in June, a replacement Halifax II and another Oxford in July, then another Hurricane and a Mitchell in August. Wroath's close links with A&AEE also enabled the casual loan of Establishment aircraft from time to time when they were not being used over the other side of the airfield.

One of the two naval pilots, Lieutenant G. P. L. Shea-Simonds, RNVR, gives some idea of the problems that would-be test pilots had had to face up to then. He had been posted to RN Air Station Hatston in the Orkneys early in 1942 and he had a jack-of-all-trades task there, being Officer in Charge of the Special Duties Flight and Workshops Test Pilot — all this after flying Sharks for Telegraphist Air Gunners to train on. The Workshops Test Pilot duty involved flying, and clearing, all the aircraft which came out of the Repair Shop at Hatston, whatever their type, and the only help he had was an official RAF book called *Manual of Advanced Flying Training* which had a few paragraphs on Maintenance Test Flying. From these few paragraphs he evolved his own system of testing the aircraft as they came out for clearance; for him, therefore, the Test Pilots' Training Flight was obviously a good way ahead. He writes:

'My Captain sent for me one day and said: "Look, Shea, it's probably time you had a move. I'm moving fairly soon and my successor is somebody I don't think you get on very well with." This was true — he was a fairly pompous gentleman and we were not exactly the best of friends. He said: "This has just come up and I think it might be your 'handwriting' " — he showed me a signal about this forthcoming test pilots' course at Boscombe Down.

'It was a great surprise and a tremendous thrill. I thought with just two chaps out of the Fleet Air Arm I hadn't a chance, but there it was.

'I think really No 1 Course can best be described as guinea pigs, which was roughly what we were, because the course developed as it went along, although there obviously had been good background planning in advance. Sammy Wroath had been given the job of running the course and Humphreys, dear old Humph, was the "Maths Master" as we called him (Sammy was the "Headmaster") and that was it. Sammy's policy was to get everybody in the air as quickly as possible, preferably on types of aircraft unlike anything they had been flying before. In my case the first flight I did from Boscombe, which I think was on the first day, was simply in the Hurricane, with which I was familiar, and that was just to look around the local area and get my bearings. The next flight I did was in a Halifax, which was a great change! Sammy's theory was that we were all meant to be fairly experienced pilots or we would not be on the Course, therefore we were to fly anything that was thrown at us. I am bound to say that this worked out in many ways. It was rather funny, actually, seeing some of our colleagues who had been in Bomber Command, really experienced drivers

of Halifaxes and Lancasters, the first time they flew the Hurricane; it was rather entertaining to watch. There was no risk to life or limb but obviously they were a little surprised as to how light these things were compared with what they were accustomed to flying. Likewise those of us who had been used to lighter aircraft found it was rather like driving a bus when we got into one of these larger machines.

'As the Course developed one became more and more involved in the aerodynamic studies and that sort of thing, which were fascinating when one got into the swing of it. I think the general principle was that the mornings were usually devoted to lectures, either from the CTO or other personnel at Boscombe with the occasional visiting lecturer from Farnborough or one of the firms, and the afternoons were given over to flying. Although the school hadn't too many aircraft of its own Sammy's influence was an enormous help because he was able to borrow and scrounge aircraft from the various test squadrons of the A&AEE, which gave us a nice cross-section of different types right through the Course.

'The Ground School activities were completely new to us. We were armed with all the basic equipment of a slide rule, notebooks and endless supplies of graph paper. From then on dear old "Humph" ran the thing in this way; he would give a lecture on, say, determining base climbing speed of an aircraft, partial climbs, what you did, what it was all in aid of, why you did it and how you presented the results in the form of a curve on the graph paper. Then in the afternoon we would go and fly the chosen aircraft, record the figures as he had told us and plot and submit our own graphs; in other words the graph was our evening prep! This applied through all the various elements of performance testing, level speeds and so on. When it came to measurements, for example, of level speeds, in addition to recording the figures in the aeroplane we were given the necessary information to enable us to reduce these results to standard from the point of view of barometric pressure, temperature and the other variables and thus present the results in the same way as would be wanted if a genuine test pilot was tossing in that information into a Tech Office. Although Boscombe Down itself was primarily concerned with performance testing we also did quite a lot of handling flying, concerned with the qualitative assessment of the aircraft from a handling point of view.

'This latter is very much more a question of the pilot's opinion, not necessarily backed up by a lot of facts in the form of figures, which was invaluable for those of us who went on to development test flying with firms afterwards. Also, having learnt so much from "Humph" the whole science of aerodynamics was not quite such a deep mystery to us; thus it enabled me to talk to all our technical shops at Supermarine on the development of the later marks of the Spitfire and the Spiteful, breaking a kind of language barrier between the boffin and the pilot'.

Shea-Simonds in fact did go into the aircraft industry, first to Westland where he was involved with production testing of Supermarine Seafires and then to Vickers-Supermarine themselves where he was involved in the development testing of the later marks of Spitfire, Seafire and the Spiteful/Seafang series.

His remarks show just how sound a foundation Wroath and Maclaren Humphreys laid right from the start, a foundation that was built upon in the years ahead. However, it also highlights one of the more revolutionary aspects of the course for the students. Normally, a pilot converting to a new type of aircraft would have an instructor to give him a conversion course, however brief. At this school they were just given a copy of the Pilot's Notes for the type they were going to fly, told to read them and then go off and fly it. Of such is flying experience made.

No 1 Course duly finished early in 1944 — one cannot say it passed out as there was no ceremony, no diplomas or certificates, the students were just posted as test pilots, mostly to British research establishments. There was a feeling amongst them that this took them away from the war then being fought, into a cushy sideline. But within a few years four of them, Wing Commander P. E. Webster, DSO, DFC, Squadron Leaders P. H. A. Simonds, J. C. S. Turner and D. D. Weightman, DFC, had been killed whilst carrying out their test pilots' tasks. The other naval officer, Commander G. R. Callingham, later returned as OC 'C' Squadron at Boscombe Down, whilst Wing Commander K. J. 'Pock' Sewell, AFC, DFM, had two further spells with ETPS, as a tutor in 1946–47 and as Chief Test Flying Instructor from 1954 to 1955. Sadly, on 11 March 1955 he was flying the first production Pembroke C1, *WV698*, one of the School's fleet, from Farnborough when the aircraft had an engine fire and crashed attempting to reach Boscombe Down; Sewell was killed.

The first course had finished and it had proved the system. Yes, as Shea-Simonds had said, they had been guinea-pigs and they had shown that the idea of a Test Pilots' School was not just some bright scheme dreamed up in London but was a useful tool for the future and worth perpetuating. So, by the confidence gained from the first course, the Training Flight became the Empire Test Pilots' School and a modest expansion took place to cater for an enlarged second course. In any case, changes had to be made for Sammy Wroath had been posted to America to join the British Joint Services Mission there. The post of Commandant was upgraded to a Group Captain post and was filled on his return from the USA by Group Captain J. F. X. McKenna, AFC, who had been test flying since before World War 2 started. It was said of him by 'Sandy' Powell: 'He was a quite wonderful person. I think technically he knew more about it than practically any test pilot in the world. He was a brilliant pilot and quite the most charming person you could wish to meet.' To assist him came Wing Commander H. P. 'Sandy' Powell, AFC, who was commanding 'C' Flight of the A&AEE, to act as Assistant Commandant. The course was to be expanded to about thirty students and the fleet to a similar number of aircraft. The title 'Empire' opened the School up to other Allied nations and when No 2 Course arrived there were eight nationalities other than British represented.

One of Powell's first acts was to obtain an adjutant; let him explain how himself:

'Something that was most important at this time — we needed an adjutant, someone of experience and understanding. We had at Boscombe Down one Fred Arnold (Flight Lieutenant F. R. Arnold). He was not young; he had been a machine-gunner in the Machine Gun Corps in World War 1, in which he had been gassed. He did twelve ops as a rear gunner with Coastal Command in World War 2, then he came to Boscombe Down as an experimental gunner in Armament Squadron and his task was trying out new guns, new ammunition and allied tasks. At a time when I was on the way with starting the test pilots' course an aeroplane crash-landed in my dispersal — everyone got out of it and we stood watching this, waiting for it to blow up and it didn't, mercifully, but a tall gentleman with a big ginger moustache got out of it carrying a gun of vast weight, an experimental gun, and it was dear Fred. He wouldn't leave that thing in the aeroplane, though it had petrol all over the place and was likely to blow up, and he staggered out with this gun.

'That evening I asked him in the Mess if it wouldn't be a bad idea (he was between fifty and sixty then) if he joined me on the School and became adjutant. I plied him with quite a large quantity of whisky without any success but after three weeks of this he weakened and gave in. He was duly posted to the School and was quite wonderful; he used to write to all the students, particularly those from overseas, so that they still kept in touch with the School.'

This was all part of the building up of the School in its enlarged status. There was a need for Maclaren Humphreys to expand the syllabus.

'This automatically grew,' he said. 'It came more mathematical on much of the theoretical side, which we kept out of the first course as much as we could — mainly because I did not know the sort of people I would have to deal with, and one didn't want to spend too much time teaching basic mathematics before starting anything else. I didn't know how much of the theoretical side they could absorb and quite often it was a question of having to do the working out myself after an exercise to help them out. On the second course I knew more of what they were able to do theoretically. We had a hand in the choice of people coming on the second course and knew what we wanted as a result of our experience on the first course — a basic knowledge of mathematics up to a certain level. It was also decided that I needed assistants; I think I had two or three staff at varying times (on No 2 Course it was one F. D. Hillson, who stayed on for Course 3 as well). To some extent I helped with the flying side as I had in fact been a Flight Test Engineer. Quite often in the two-seater aircraft I sat in the second seat and as far as I was concerned this was just an extension of what I had been doing before — except these people were brand new to it! I was able, because of my experience as a Flight Test Engineer, to tell them what I wanted.

'One student had done three operational tours and the one thing I had the greatest difficulty in getting him to do was to fly the aeroplane at full throttle. As far as I was concerned this was a normal daily routine —one was allowed to fly flat out at that time for five minutes which, of course, as part of his operational flying was one of the last things he ever did and then only in a dire emergency. I well remember that each time I did this exercise the beads of perspiration stood out on his forehead; he was absolutely terrified. It took quite a while to persuade him to do it.'

Sandy Powell had the job of expanding the flying side, acquiring more aircraft, being responsible for most of the lecturing on that side of the house and setting up his own ground crew. To do this he robbed his old Flight in 'C' Squadron of the best airmen and set it up under a quite remarkable fitter, Flight Sergeant C. Rutter. Powell later put him up for an MBE and Warrant Officer both of which came through. The aircraft fleet eventually expanded [see accompanying diagram]. The students came rolling in too, eleven RAF officers, three from the Navy, one Australian, two Canadian, one South African, two from the USAAF, a Norwegian, a Pole and two Chinese. So, straight away there were

By 1944 the Training Flight had become the Empire Test Pilots' School, a name emblazoned on the huts containing the students' classrooms, standing alongside the original Nissen huts. Obviously someone had endeavoured to brighten up the grim appearance with neatly laid out flower beds.

The interior of these huts resembled the seedier sort of private preparatory schools of the twenties and thirties with poor lighting, crabby old desks, damp seeping through the walls. This is 1945, with No 3 Course. Maclaren Humphreys is explaining something to Squadron Leader E. B. Gale, AFC, of the RCAF. The civilian behind the lantern is Ron Clear, of Airspeed, and the naval lieutenant on the left is Peter Twiss, the first British pilot to fly the Fairey FD2 at over 1,000 mph.

language problems, both in the air and in the lectures, particularly with the two Chinese, Captains Chen and Loh. Students came from industry, too, including Jimmy Orrell of Avro who wrote:

'I was sent on No 2 Course in 1944, and I must say I had an enjoyable year there because my experience already in test flying rather put me in a different category from the other people. I found myself, when it came to the Lancaster, flying as the tutor rather than one of the students. An amusing incident took place with Mike Lithgow (who went on to be well known for his experiences and for test flying) when we first reported. It was suggested that Mike Lithgow might come with me in an Oxford because he hadn't been in a twin aircraft and flying around I was letting him have a bash at it and then it came to the landing, and the engines wouldn't play ball — wouldn't drag us into the airfield so I landed it on a ploughed field just before the boundary. As we were coming in Mike Lithgow was about to raise the undercarriage, which was the Service's requirement when force landing — I slapped his hand and said "Don't do that" — landed in the ploughed field and kept the aircraft in one piece, much to Mike Lithgow's surprise. The Commandant at that time was McKenna and he said "Thank you very much, Jimmy, for not breaking our aeroplane on the first day of flying — we can recover it from the ploughed field." '

Conditions were not all they might be. Sqn Ldr R. E. Havercroft, one of the RAF students, recalls:

'Food was poor at Boscombe Down. It was very crowded there, accommodation was bad, people sleeping three to a room and it was not at all nice, particularly for those chaps who had perhaps come across from other countries where they had still been living on the fat of the land, like the United States, and to come to beans for breakfast today, tomorrow and the day after . . . !

'Most of us, anyway, used to go into what we called the wind-tunnel afterwards — that was the bar. It used to be in the front of the Mess, up the steps into the lobby — the bar was right opposite. The bar was right in front and the wind used to howl down the corridor in the winter-time and it was just like a ruddy wind-tunnel. We used to sit there shivering, drinking our beer, but tremendous parties used to brew up in that corridor, with all those chaps drinking away — because, you see, not only TPs but the squadrons and A&AEE itself were beavering away as well, and the visitors we used to get — it was marvellous. I've seen General Smuts there, Lord Trenchard, Sir Archibald Sinclair, so many of them. Lots of pranks and fun, playing games on the floor.'

With the wealth of talent amongst the students the school used many of the students themselves to convert each other on to types with which they were familiar, thus saving time. Quoting Havercroft again:

'The technical side was always dealt with by MH (Maclaren Humphreys) and he would lay down a programme of Why you did it, How you did it, on the blackboard in the classroom. Then Sandy Powell would tell you the technique of doing it in the aircraft itself.'

This, plus the theoretical lectures, always took place in the morning then the afternoons would be set aside for flying which had given Rutter's empire all the morning to persuade the aircraft to come serviceable. Havercroft remembers:

'We would do partial climbs, stability, roll performance, yaw performance, handling in dives, handling in the stall, spinning, cockpit assessment. You had to take the aircraft through these exercises, bring back your results on your knee pad and then get down and work out quantitatively the results and then plot them on graphs, working out all the results which would be kept in a folder as part of your course. The reports were given to MH and he would check them and write an assessment — "This is good, not good enough, what about this, did you do that?" SP would do the same from a flying standpoint.

'If there was an aircraft we hadn't flown very much on the course we would do a complete handling assessment and for several days would fly the aircraft and examine all aspects and go through the flight envelope, as far as one could — then write a complete comprehensive report on it as if on "A" flight, the performance testing squadron, and had been asked to do the same thing for a prototype aircraft. It was all good fun and it was the evaluation of a particular aircraft as you would probably have to do it if you were posted to a testing establishment in your own country after the course was over, and many of us did just that. I was posted back to ''A'' flight.'

Another innovation was introduced towards the end of this course, one which has stood the test of time. Each student was given an aircraft, usually one which he had flown but little during the course, and he had to do a complete handling assessment on that aircraft. For several days he would fly the aircraft, examining all aspects of it and taking it through its flight envelope. This was followed by a complete and comprehensive report which was submitted (rather on the lines of a thesis, although a very practical one). This latter acitivity was a worthwhile exercise, for many of the students would go on to do just that on posting from ETPS.

The Course at that time was a very varied affair with the first four months spent at Boscombe Down on the lectures and flying as outlined above. The fifth and sixth months were spent at the RAE in Farnborough where it toured the various departments and were able as far as possible to see flight tests in connection with those Departments' experiments. It also included such items as an Oxygen Course and Flying Clothing at the Physiology Laboratory. This was followed by a month making visits to aircraft, engine and propeller firms and by the pilots being detached to various firms to take part in routine test flying for a month. The final month involved the students being attached to the various Flights at the A&AEE, Boscombe Down, getting involved in the normal work on their Flight.

Sandy Powell comments:

'I always make the best mistakes! I thought we would do the work first and would reserve two months for going around the aircraft industry, and that would be over the winter

Permanent staff, on moving to Cranfield in October, 1945. Left to Right: Wing Commander H. P. 'Sandy' Powell, AFC (CTFI); Mr Maclaren Humphreys, BSc, AFRAeS, AInstp, (CGI); Flight Lieutenant F. R. Arnold, Adjutant.

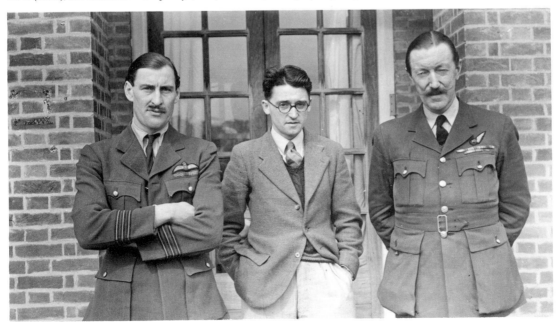

period when you can't do much flying. But every firm we went to, and of course there were about twenty-eight firms in the country then, laid on a directors' lunch and a test pilots' evening and it was only a few days and we were a bunch of wrecks. The firms all pushed the boat out because they wanted to find new test pilots.'

Maclaren Humphreys adds:

'It was a firm decision right from the beginning that we should have an extended visit to Farnborough as well as a period of visiting around the firms. At that time it was all done in one lump so people left off flying completely for a period of a couple of months which later, quite rightly, was decided the wrong way to do it.

It was very heavy going. We went to Rolls-Royce and we visited Derby first. We had dinner in the evening at Derby and lunch the following day at Hucknall. They had done us so well we thought the least we could do was to do something about reciprocating. We invited quite a lot of the Rolls people to come back to the hotel with us, which turned into a dreadful orgy. The following day we were due to visit A. V. Roe at Manchester and arrived at the Grand Hotel at about six o'clock — most of us feeling terrible and thinking thank goodness we have a night's rest ready for A. V. Roe tomorrow. About 6.30 pm I had a 'phone call from the then Chief Test Pilot to welcome us and to say they would all be over at eight o'clock for a dinner which they had arranged. So there we were until about two o'clock

Factory visits were a feature of the courses early on — No 2 Course is here visiting the Rotol propeller factory in Gloucestershire with Mac Humphreys taking over a piece of equipment and demonstrating it to Captain C. T. Loh of the Chinese Air Force, whilst Squadron Leader Zurakowski of the Polish Air Force looks on.

Embryo test pilots in the making, on another factory visit. No 4 Course in 1946.

the following morning! It was almost like that all the way through.'

One of the idiosyncrasies of the early courses was the barking tradition. This originated with Sandy Powell's dog, Joe, a black and white collie. This dog would sit on the platform beside Powell when he was lecturing and if anyone asked the Wing Commander such a difficult question that there was a pause, the dog would bark back at the questioner. Whilst he was there every generation of test pilots (Mike Lithgow started it) would bark and then all the aspiring test pilots would bark at each other. Of such stuff are traditions made. The collie, however, loved flying and one of the Chinese, Chen, was most alarmed one day when, on getting into a Spitfire, the dog landed on his lap assuming he was Powell. Needless to say the barking tradition was enacted on some of the more festive nights and on one occasion, after a combined 'do' with Fairey and Hawker, it was introduced to the constabulary of

Windsor by Mike and Sandy — the police were not amused!

About the course itself, Havercroft tells us:

'The Chinese had both language and experience problems; they had nothing resembling operational experience. They were brilliant at maths, they could leave most of us standing at that. Sometimes MH had to launch into equations and a certain amount of trig; Chen and Loh would immediately switch on and talk to him on the blackboard in terms of maths and they would get on together like a house on fire. There was no communism in those days, they were part of the free Air Force. Chen was a jolly little fat man, always smiling and Loh was a thinner, sallow-faced chap.'

Wing Commander Powell mentioned this fact:

'I learned a little about the Chinese from my father. If we had turned them down as having failed the course they would probably have done something terrible to them. I wrote an impassioned letter to the Air Attaché saying that it was solely due to the language difficulty that we could not pass them in one year, but we would welcome them for a second year.'

Even in those days the course cost about £10,000 but the Chinese were quite happy for them to stay.

The Course was not without tragedy. The Commandant himself, 'Sam' McKenna, was testing a Mustang when a gun panel flew off during a high speed dive and the aircraft went straight into the ground. Two students were killed during the duration

Group Captain J. F. X. McKenna, AFC, who returned from America to be Commandant of the second Course and of whom Sandy Powell wrote: 'He was a quite wonderful person. I think that technically he knew more about it than practically any test pilot in the world.' Sadly, he was killed whilst flying a Mustang during the period of the first course.

of the course, Flight Lieutenant N. J. Bonner, AFC, of the RAF and Flight Lieutenant L. R. Brady, RAAF, and the Canadian Squadron Leader R. M. Mace was killed in a flying accident to a Lancaster in December 1944.

No 2 Course included three test pilots from industry whom the firms had sent to benefit their test flying capabilities. From Bristol came John Northway, to be killed in 1949 in a Bristol Freighter accident. From Avro came Jimmy Orrell who went on to a long and successful test career at Woodford and from Miles at Reading came the colourful Ken Waller. Ken, never without his trilby hat, had been a flying instructor pre-war at the fashionable Brooklands School of Flying. He had, with Owen Catchcart-Jones, flown one of the three revolutionary de Havilland Comet racers in the England-Australia Race in 1934, coming in fourth even after getting lost in Persia (Iran) and forced landing there. During the war he flew as test pilot for Miles Aircraft.

The Course included not a few whose names became familiar in the aviation world after the war. The South African, Major Adams, eventually rose to great heights in South African Airways; Squadron Leader S. E. Esler was foremost in high-speed flight testing and was killed flying the very first delta-winged aircraft, the Avro 707, in September 1949. Squadron Leader Eric Franklin had already flown two tours of bomber operations and two tours of testing at Boscombe Down before joining No 2 Course. With the course over he obtained release from the Service to rejoin Armstrong Whitworth, with whom he had been a pre-war apprentice, and served as their Chief Test Pilot into the 1960s, being the pilot who flew the very advanced AW52 twin-jet flying wing in 1948.

Lieutenant Commander Mike Lithgow went on to join Vickers-Supermarine and became their Chief Test Pilot, flying all their post-war swept-wing fighters and gaining the World's Speed Record at 735 mph (1,183 km/h) on a Swift F Mk 4 in September 1953. Being Mike it was inevitable that, with one of the Chinese on the course called Loh, he dubbed the two Chinese Left-Wing-Loh and Right-Wing-High and so they were nicknamed throughout the Course. Mike later transferred to the British Aircraft Corporation at Weybridge to test fly the new One-Eleven airliner and was killed when the first prototype entered a deep stall in October 1963 and crashed.

Lieutenant Colonel J. R. Muehlberg of the USAF was intrumental in setting up, on his return, the first Test Pilots' School in the United States, inevitably building upon his experience with ETPS. Two of No 2 Course became test pilots with the engine firm Armstrong-Siddeley after the war; they were Squadron Leader Waldo Price-Owen, who came to Boscombe Down with a background of fighter operations in the Middle East and the United Kingdom, and Jim Starky, a New Zealander who had been a Lancaster pilot. Finally, mention must be made of 'Zura' — Squadron Leader J. Zurakowski, the Pole who joined Gloster as a test pilot after leaving ETPS and whose demonstrations with the Meteor on one engine became a byword in the late 1940s and early 1950s. He later went to Avro Canada and was responsible for the development flying of the CF-100 Canuck and CF-105 Arrow.

The first Course had shown that there was a point and purpose in training pilots for test flying and that, in fact, such training was feasible. The second Course, a full one, had made clear that the School was on the right lines and that the formula that had been established needed but little modification to be right for future courses. On this basis No 3 Course was recruited. Only minor modifications were made in the shape of the course, such as splitting up the visits to the industry. The most

important task was to enrol a new Commandant to take the place of Sam McKenna. Although he had only served for part of a course, such was his test flying skill and his towering personality that he impressed his mark indelibly on the School in the time he was its Commandant. His memory is perpetuated by the McKenna Trophy which is awarded annually to the most outstanding student on the course.

His successor was Group Captain H. J. Wilson, AFC. Wilson had, for most of the war, been the doyen of the test pilots at Farnborough and had played a large part in evaluating German aircraft as they were captured. He was also involved in the first Wing of RAF jet fighters, Meteor F 3s, as their Wing Commander Flying and it was from this task that he came to be Commandant. During his time with ETPS, quite as a sideline almost, he flew the cleaned-up Meteor F 4 to break the World's Speed Record at 606 mph (975 km/h) on 7 November 1945. He was not the rather flamboyant character that McKenna had been but was an extremely fine and meticulous test pilot and his three years in the Commandant's chair at ETPS established it on a steady course for the future.

For No 3 Course not only was 'Willie' Wilson the new boy in the Commandant's chair but the staff retained Mr Hillson and was enhanced by posting in Squadron Leader E. E. Collins, DSO, DFM, to assist Sandy Powell, and appointing F. J. Irving to assist both with the classroom work and as a Technical Observer for some of the flying sequences. No 3 Course was, again largely RAF, though with five naval pilots this time and two from the US Navy joining two each from the USAF, Canadian, Australian, New Zealand Air Forces, together with one each from Belgium, France and the Netherlands. Again the industry participated with W. G. M. Sanders from Handley Page and Ron Clear from Airspeed. And, of course, Chen and · Loh were there, too.

The Course proceeded with very few alarms and excursions. The only fatality was one of the two Americans, Major Everett Leach, who was killed on a test sortie over the Isle of Wight in an Airspeed Oxford. His companion, Major Ralph Hoewing, had come with him to Boscombe Down from Wright Field as the result of a visit from Colonel Warburton who had been most impressed by what he had seen at ETPS and inaugurated the USAF Test Pilots School at Edwards, under the command of Major Muehlberg who had been on No 2 Course. Ralph Hoewing eventually succeeded him in command on his return to the USA in 1946. Hoewing remembers one hair-raising flight whilst on the Course which happened during his visit to Farnborough. Because he had flown a captured Focke-Wulf Fw 190 several times at Wright Field, he volunteered when a pilot was needed to fly a Fw 190 from Farnborough to an RAF airfield near Oxford.

'Take-off was uneventful,' he remembers, 'but I was having trouble operating the landing gear handle. A glance down inside the cockpit solved the problem and the gear raised. Looking out I saw nothing but clouds! I was totally unprepared for instrument flight, was at 300 ft in cloud in an unfamiliar aircraft with altimeter and ASI in kilometres. I kept the airspeed constant and climbed straight and topped out at 8,000 feet.' Keeping going on the same heading as he set out he eventually spiralled down through a hole in the clouds, discovered where he was and landed. 'Yes, the good Lord does watch over the foolhardy!' was his final comment.

Two of the Continentals went back to important tasks in their own countries, Lieutenant Commander J. V. B. 'Hugo' Burgherhout, DSO, Royal Netherlands Navy, took up test-flying with Fokker after his release and Flight Lieutenant J. N. M. Le Grand, CdeG, became Chief Test Pilot to the Belgian Government. Squadron Leader C. Coton, DFC, returned to ETPS in 1948 as a Flying Tutor and in that year, and the subsequent one, was the Chief Test Flying Instructor. Flight Lieutenant J. O. Lancaster came to ETPS after two bomber tours, on Wellingtons and Lancasters, and a period at A&AEE. After the course was over he joined Boulton Paul as a test pilot at Wolverhampton, moving soon to Saunders-Roe where he helped Geoffrey Tyson to test the A1 jet flying-boat (now on display at the Imperial War Museum collection at Duxford). In 1949 he moved to the firm with whom he had carried out an apprenticeship, Armstrong Whitworth, joining Eric Franklin on the testing of the AW52 Flying-Wing aircraft and whilst engaged in this made history by being the first pilot to use a Martin-Baker ejector seat for real. The AW52 had set up such violent longitudinal oscillations that he was fast losing consciousness so he ejected successfully.

Squadron Leader C. G. B. McClure, AFC, went on afterwards to serve at the College of Aeronautics at Cranfield whence the School moved in 1946. He remembers being innocently the cause of Sandy Powell getting into hot water. He confesses that:

'It was in March 1945 that I borrowed an aeroplane (a Harvard) to fly up to Riccall to visit my wife's brother at nearby Selby for a weekend. I walked back to the airfield on Monday morning — I couldn't see my Harvard where I had left it and Air Traffic said: "Oh dear, sorry, but a Halifax coming back off ops slid across the airfield right into your Harvard and wrote it off". That, of course, stopped anybody borrowing an aircraft for the weekend.'

One of the naval aviators on the course

Outside the huts the ETPS fleet awaits the day's flying. The line comprises Dominie I *HG715*, Tiger Moth *T6831*, Swordfish III *HS642* and two Oxfords, and was taken in 1945.

was Peter Twiss. After an eventful war, principally in the Mediterranean flying Hurricanes, Fulmars and Seafires, during which he gained a DSC and Bar, he ended up at Boscombe Down on the Intensive Flying Unit bringing the Fairey Firefly into service. This was followed by a posting to Washington as part of the British Air Mission. From there he went to ETPS and gravitated to Fairey after the course. He stayed with them during which time he flew many different types until they gave up flying. He was primarily involved in the FD2, the high speed delta which was the most advanced airframe built in the United Kingdom in the 1950s. In it he broke the World's Absolute Speed Record on 10 March 1956, raising it to 1,132 mph (1,821 km/h), 300 mph (483 km/h) faster than that achieved by an American F-100C Super Sabre the year before. But previously he had had a near-disaster in the aircraft when, at 30,000 ft (9,144 m) and thirty miles (48 km) from Boscombe, his RR Avon engine 'went out' on him and he had to make a 'dead-stick' landing with no air

brakes or nose-droop, at a speed of 230 knots.

Ron Clear, one of the civilian test pilots (from Airspeed) on the Course, describes what it did for him:

'When offered the Course by George Errington, our Chief Test Pilot, it did occur to me that were I to fail to graduate I could hardly expect to return to Airspeed as a professional! As for the benefits that I derived from my ETPS Course I can only say that they were enormous. Prior to joining the Course I had notched up some 1,300 hours test flying on eight widely varying types from the Horsa military glider (and its associated tugs — the Whitley and Halifax) to the Seafire and Mosquito. This background of practical experience could now be married to an excellent technical training with which it was complementary. A further benefit stemmed from the many enthusiastic discussions with other students and all ETPS staff — in particular with dear "old" Maclaren Humphreys ("Humph") — during many hours of extra curricular coaching so willingly given.

'The apparent inconsistencies between inflexible design requirements and ideal handling characteristics gradually became understandable; why the demands of a purist aerodynamicist needed to be treated with caution and weighed against the advice and experience of a good design engineer! For me, it made the "eternal compromise" a hard but acceptable fact of life. This was particularly evident in the field of stability and control.

'I was fascinated by the critical balance between an economic disaster and a viable competitive design, where so much could be gained from so little yet so little could be gained from so much; where sound advice from a good test pilot was vital.

'I little realised how much this experience was to hold me in very good stead for many years to come — in a multitude of different situations from test flying, demonstration flying and even training.

'In hindsight it was largely responsible for allowing me to extend my test flying career to a total of 38 years, and enable me to enjoy the challenge of flying over 100 types and clock up 12,000 hours!'

Thus passed off No 3 Course but already the writing was on the wall for ETPS at Boscombe. Maclaren Humphreys explained why:

The fast single-engined fleet outside the entire ETPS accomodation at Boscombe Down in August 1945. This part of the fleet comprises two Spitfire IXs, one Spitfire F 21s, three Tempest F 5s, three Tempest F 2s and three Harvard T 2Bs.

'During the second course at Boscombe Down they started building the first runway there, the main runway, and things were getting a bit cluttered. Willie Wilson, in particular, thought we would be better off going somewhere else where we wouldn't be tied up with a lot of other flying — Boscombe was a fairly busy airfield. We just looked around for a vacant airfield and at that time the war in Europe had finished and airfields were becoming available. The airfield at Cranfield was vacant but it was known that the College of Aeronautics was going to come in — it was thought that it would be a good thing so that we could help the utilisation of the airfield which the College perhaps wouldn't have that much use for.'

The College of Aeronautics was one of the bright new ideas stemming from the vast expansion in aeronautics during the war and the need to train a whole range of men academically for post-war careers in aviation. It was felt that such a move might provide spin-off both for the College and the School as a result of the interaction between the two. So, with No 3 Course finished, the Empire Test Pilots' School packed its bags and in October 1945 made the move up to Cranfield in Bedfordshire.

CHAPTER 3
Post-War Expansion

Although performing a recognisably useful function the School had, up till now, been looked upon by many as something of a nuisance at Boscombe and already there had been quite some upheavals there during the 1944 and 1945 courses whilst the main runway was being built, with the consequent cluttering and disorganisation. Group Captain Wilson also had views about the disruption caused to his training schedules by the priority given to A&AEE flying and he felt, no doubt with some justification, that the School would be better off somewhere on its own where it could 'do its own thing' without let or hindrance. With the war over and the contraction of the RAF accelerating there should be no real problem in finding a vacant airfield, although there might be greater difficulties in persuading the authorities that such a move was justified and the expense worth the effort.

Throughout 1945 much hard work behind the scenes was being expended in this task and one likely possibility was the airfield at Cranfield in Bedfordshire. This had been built pre-war so had ample domestic and maintenance accommodation — large Type 'C' hangars built in 1936 and comfortable officers' and airmen's living quarters and Messes. However, it was known that the bold new project labelled the College of Aeronautics was going to be set up there.

This College was to be something of a combination of technical college and university to train personnel to take Britain's aviation industry into the major stages of progress which lay just ahead.

So the College would use many of the buildings and workshops whilst having little or no use for the airfield, whereas ETPS would make maximum use of the airfield whilst their classroom and servicing requirements would be relatively modest. It was thought, too, that the interchange of ideas between the College and the School in the Mess and elsewhere would benefit both organisations. Eventually, these ideas came to fruition and the School was consigned to the Ministry of Supply.

On 15 October 1945 a small advance party went north from Boscombe to lay down the foundations of the move. Three days later the main party followed up by road and took over the accommodation; Flying Officer L. N. Flower, DFC, and the incomparable Warrant Officer C. Rutter, MBE, took charge of the hangar allocated to ETPS and in a very short time had it cleaned out and set up ready for the arrival of the aircraft. Squadron Leader W. R. Morris, AFC, took charge of the aircraft and equipment which eventually flew up before the end of the month, leaving Fred Arnold, the Adjutant, behind for the moment to clear up all the paperwork at Boscombe. The move was slightly complicated by the fact that the Commandant, Group Captain Wilson, was away at Manston with his high-speed Meteor F 4s, plus the School's Meteor F 3s, busily establishing a new World's Air Speed Record. He eventually turned up with it in his pocket.

Preparations were now in hand for No 4 Course which would be arriving in the New Year. This was to be a slightly bigger

Course than previously with 37 students, and all, except one Canadian, were from the British Air Forces (RAF and RN). It was estimated that the Course at this time cost £10,000 per student. The aircraft fleet was changing, too, not all the 1945 aircraft moving up to Cranfield and some notable additions were posted in. There was naturally a greater accent on jet aircraft, with the additional Meteors and a couple of Vampire F 1s. Oxfords and Harvards continued to be the staple advanced trainers. Lancasters and Spitfires were also indispensible but there was a greater influx of post-war naval types with a bunch of Fireflies and a Seafire 46, quite the most fearsome version of the Spitfire yet to fly and a terror to those pilots whose previous experience had been largely on the four-engined heavies. In fact, the 1946 line-up looked as follows:

2 × Airspeed Oxford T 1
2 × Hawker Tempest F 2
3 × Supermarine Spitfire F 9
2 × de Havilland Vampire F 1
1 × Gloster Meteor F 1
3 × Gloster Meteor F 3
1 × Grunau Baby glider
1 × de Havilland Tiger Moth T 2
4 × Fairey Firefly FR 1
3 × Avro Lancaster B 1
1 × Douglas Dakota C 3
1 × Avro Lincoln B 2
3 × North American Harvard T 2B
1 × Supermarine Seafire F 46
1 × Avro Anson C 19
1 × de Havilland Dominie C 1
1 × Douglas Boston B 3
1 × Supermarine Spitfire F 21
1 × Lockheed Hudson C 3

Such a diverse array of types gave students a very wide range of experience and idiosyncrasies with which to cope and be able to understand and evaluate which,

of course, was one of the purposes of the flying.

After Boscombe Down the living arrangements were much more comfortable with peacetime accommodation, classrooms and hangar. Although the food was not as one would now expect it, rationing still being in force, the Mess Manager who, legend has it, had been Edward, Prince of Wales' Gentleman's Gentleman, had very good contacts, like nearby Woburn, so when the meat ration ran out venison would arrive as a substitute.

All the students who arrived for No 4 Course had 'above average' assessments as pilots and at least 3,000 hours' pilot time but in most cases this was on only a few types and these would largely be stereotyped into one class of aircraft, say, heavy bombers or flying-boats. On arrival at Cranfield they were expected to fly every type in the ETPS fleet and, as can be seen from the above list, this provided every one of them with some considerable challenges. To add to this problem, the only types that could really be used for conversion flying, with dual controls, were the Harvard and Oxford so these were used, the Harvard to convert 'heavies' pilots to the quirks of single-engined machines and the Oxford to acquaint the fighter boys with two or more engines and their drawbacks. To move on up to four engines the School relied on the advice of students on the Course who had four-motor experience. As Havercroft recalls:

'It was necessary to launch a student off into the blue in a type with which he was quite unfamiliar except for a cockpit briefing and a knowledge of the engine and airframe limitations and emergency procedures read up from the Pilots' Notes.'

There was, therefore, a considerable potential safety problem in extending the students' experience for the purpose of completing the flying syllabus. It says much, therefore, for the calibre of the students selected and the quality of the briefings given by the staff that there were no serious accidents on this Course.

The Course began in January and ran through intensively until May when it was suddenly ended. Twenty-four of the students were hurriedly passed out of what was termed a short course, having learnt the rudiments of performance testing but little more and were posted, most of them, to Boscombe Down. Amongst them were several who, within a few years, would give their lives in developing the new generation of British aircraft — Squadron Leader P. G. Evans, DFC, in a Hastings in 1948; Squadron Leader P. J. Garner in a Wyvern in 1947; Squadron Leader K. A. Major, DFC, in the Saunders Roe SR A/1 jet flying-boat in 1949. Others have stayed within the aircraft . world throughout their careers and made significant contributions in one way and another. A young naval Lieutenant on this Course was D. P. Davies, DSC, who has since become well-known as the Chief Test Pilot of the ARB and CAA and whose analytical certifications of aircraft like the Boeing 707 added to its safety considerably. Probably his greatest achievement in this field was master-minding the flying of the certification programme of the Concorde 'with' Gordon Corps thus taking civil airline certification into entirely new realms. Another Lieutenant, Nick Goodhart, ended up as a Rear Admiral and achieved much in the field of gliding. The naval contingent on this Course was obviously a vintage selection for it also contained Lieutenant K. R. Hickson who returned as a Captain in 1960 to be ETPS Commandant and later was Superintendent of Flying at RAE Bedford.

'A new idea was introduced in No 4 Course to combat the shortcomings for those students having to cope with widely differing types of aircraft outside their previous experience. This was the appointment of Flying Tutors, two of them, whose task was to supervise more closely the progress and problems of the students placed under their care. It enabled the students to obtain closer supervision of their flying and to have someone to discuss their difficulties with as the Course progressed. At first the tutors were not allocated to specific students, neither did they give in-flight instruction on test flying techniques. These latter points, which were weaknesses in the overall supervision of the training, were remedied on No 6 Course.

'The tutorial system, was especially valuable for those foreign students whose first language was not English. For every hour spent in the air the student would be faced with three to four hours of written work in the preparation of his records (analysing, reducing and plotting his notes during flying) and writing his reports. Foreign students found this a major hurdle, having to do it in an unfamiliar language and sometimes using measurements of a different system to that which they used. Others, even reasonably able in English, found difficulties in expressing their ideas coherently and recording them logically. For all these situations the flying tutor was able to come in and assist. His task was to grasp whether the student had actually understood the implications of the test he had carried out and could record them in a lucid way, understandable to those who read the reports. By being able to discuss these matters with a tutor, the student was immeasurably helped.

'Another matter that was properly tackled at Cranfield was the type conversion to four-engined aircraft.

A pre-flight check, posed for the photographers. In the cockpit of this Vampire F 1 is Squadron Leader H. G. Hastings, AFC, AFM, being overlooked by the Commandant, Group Captain H. J. Wilson, AFC. Looking on are left to right: Mr J. C. Miles of the DAP of Australia; Lieutenant R. B. Giblin, DFC, US Navy and Squadron Leader M. Kondolefas of the Royal Hellenic Air Force. it is at Cranfield in 1946 and No 5 Course.

The School now had not only a Lancaster but a Lincoln and these types were normally flown by a crew of two pilots, a navigator and a flight engineer. For No 5 Course two Qualified Flying Instructors (QFIs) were posted in together with two navigators and two flight engineers so that any student flying these types could have the benefit of an experienced crew, whereas heretofore they tended to be left to struggle with the type unaided.'

Those who were not summarily passed into the testing world were retained as students on the next, No 5, Course. They were joined by a more normal mix of British and foreign personnel with Canadian, Australian, American, Dutch, Greek and Chinese pilots. For No 5 Course the instructional staff was strengthened by the addition of two qualified flying instructors, two navigators and two flight engineers all qualified on Lancasters and Lincolns. Four Flying Tutors were appointed, all of them Squadron Leader rank and with recent test flying experience at Boscombe Down.

One of these flying tutors appointed for No 5 Course was Squadron Leader R. E. Havercroft; let him take up the story:

'When you came to Cranfield and you were posted to ETPS it looked marvellous because the whole place was ETPS and the Commandant was also the Station Commander. There was a feeling of pride in the Unit, you know, and there were more aircraft to fly and better ones as well. The Spitfire V had now been replaced by a Mark 22, which was the latest of the Spitfires and we had Meteors, Vampires and naval aircraft as well; so there was a lot more scope for the students. We did not have the syndicate system then nor did we fly with the students on their exercises. We were still scribbling on knee pads, using stop watches with meat hooks for measuring stick force per "g" — if you were pulling 2 g on 3 lb, well, it was three divided by two. That was the state of the test flying art in those days at Cranfield, still very elementary. There were still no proper recording boxes in which to get good accurate measurements: the only way to do it was to use the flying panel of the aircraft and these rather crude instruments.'

Maclaren Humphreys had now got into his stride and each Course found he had tightened up the ground school, abandoning material which he found was really not relevant and concentrating all along on perfecting the teaching.

'We still did visits to the aircraft companies — the aircraft manufacturing system was still very much intact even though it was a year or two after the war. They were still producing aircraft in large numbers and it was very interesting to go to Rolls-Royce and see the engines, the Merlins and so on, being turned out there and the jet engines coming in. We talked about what was on the cards — supersonic flight, more advanced fast high-flying systems, so it was still a very useful exercise to go and visit these firms and talk to the test pilots. Some of them, of course, had been through ETPS in the earlier days and were now in the companies so the visits were occasions of good social get-togethers as well!

'Most people lived in the Mess and every evening we got together in the bar, sat down together at dinner — social life was still concentrated in the Mess. After dinner most of the students had to go back and swot and write up their exercises in readiness for tomorrow. The Staff would get together and sort out the daily programme, depending on aircraft availability. Relations were very good between staff and students; we used to visit the local pubs with the students and talk out problems with them.'

During this Course the Commandant changed from 'Willie' Wilson to Group Captain S. R. Ubee, AFC, another test pilot of past renown whose flying was in no way impeded by his wearing an eye patch over his right eye. Because of its late inception the Course went on into the early weeks of 1947, the most devastating winter for very many years and many RAF stations all but closed down due to the

Dummy deck-landings were flown on the runway at Cranfield. Here a student has just been given the 'cut' command by the DLCO as he lands Firefly FR 1 PP641 on No 5 Course.

severity of the conditions. In fact one such, Binbrook in Lincolnshire, was cut off and had to have supplies dropped to it by air. Not only the snow but gales harassed the country, particularly at Cranfield. Let the Station Duty Officer relate the events:

'There was a great deal of snow in March, 1947 and all flying was stopped for many days. I recall that I was able to touch the top of a snow-drift when leaning out of a window on the top floor of the Officers' Mess. It measured thirteen feet from top to bottom. My little car, a 1937 Morris Eight, was buried for five days after I became stranded on the approach road from Bedford. The snow started to melt at the end of the month.

'One evening, as SDO, I was passing the evening in the bar; we had not received a gale warning but I had checked all the aircraft (which were dispersed outside) were into wind and tethered with controls locked. At about 9 pm I became aware that the wind had risen and was becoming violent; I telephoned the Orderly Officer and told him to turn out the Duty Crew. We drove out to the grass area where the aircraft were parked — it was very dark. The wind was now so strong that we could not stand up and had to approach the aircraft stooping or crawling on hands and knees to avoid being blown over. The noise and buffeting was frightening; we could not convey any orders for the wind sound was a deep booming note overlaid by a shrill screaming whistle.

'In the light of torches and vehicle headlights we could see the aircraft straining and rocking violently. The air was thick with flying spume and slush. The propeller of one of the Lancasters was turning against compression and this aircraft, in its tail-down attitude, was nearly flying; the tricycle undercarriage aircraft were taking it better. The light training aircraft were having a bad time and it was clear that the control locks were not standing up to the strain. Obviously it was too late to take any action other than tightening the tethering ropes and re-adjusting the chocks. We were forced to return to the shelter of the hangars which themselves were taking a heavy battering until the wind died down in the early hours of the morning. Of the twenty aircraft outside nine received damage beyond the capacity of the unit to repair, I believe that one was actually written off. The met instruments showed that the gale had gusted up to 88 mph.'

These were the prevailing conditions as No 5 Course departed and No 6 Course assembled. Amongst those leaving were Neville Duke, who was soon to become a household name as Hawker's Chief Test Pilot for the development of the Hunter, with which he planted some of the most accurate and telling sonic booms at various air displays until such disportments were banned as nuisances, and costly ones at that, considering the mounting claims for shattered greenhouses. His test career was cut short by a severe back injury in a forced landing but not until he had briefly captured the World Speed Record of 727 mph (1,170 km/h) on 7 September 1953 in the prototype Hunter *WB188* off the Sussex coast.

No 6 Course arrived, as we have seen, to the disruption of the worst weather for many years and nine of the School's aircraft *hors-de-combat*. They also knew that halfway through the course the School was taking up its belongings and moving lock-stock and barrel to Farnborough. The Staff now comprised the Commandant, Group Captain Ubee, CO; Flying Commander F. M. A. Torrens-Spence, DSO,

DSC, AFC; three Tutors, Squadron Leaders K. J. Sewell, AFC, DFM, R. E. Havercroft, AFC and E. N. M. Sparks, DFC; two QFIs, Flight Lieutenants K. E. Walters, AFC, and P. F. Wingate, DFC; and an Engineer Officer, Flight Lieutenant R. E. Humphreys. The ground instruction was in the hands of 'Humph', assisted by Mr J. A. Lawford and the Admin was looked after by Flight Lieutenant Fred Arnold and Flying Officer I. N. Flower, DFC, whilst Squadron Leader E. J. Watts, MBE, as CTO, kept the aircraft airborne. This Course was predominantly British with just two US Navy officers, a South African and an Australian. The aircraft fleet stayed much the same as before except that the School, which had long wanted to encourage gliding as an extra-curricular activity and had acquired an ex-German glider soon after arriving at Cranfield, now officially obtained a couple of Olympias, *VV400* and *VV401*, which were to serve the School for over twenty years.

Much was crammed into the first four months. Ray Watts, who came as a Squadron Leader on this Course and returned as a Group Captain in 1962 as Commandant, describes the life of early 1947:

The School put up a formation of its aircraft (and tutors) in 1947 for the benefit of a Press visit. From front to rear: Vampire F 1, Meteor F 3, Spitfire F 9C, Tempest F 2, Mosquito T 3 and Lancaster B 3.

'The Course, when I attended it, was operated on a totally different basis from that which I tried to encourage in the 'sixties. It was really trying to broaden your experience on aircraft with the minimum preparation and there were certain individuals who would withhold Pilots' Notes until the evening before you were going to fly and then toss them to you and say "You had better read that tonight — you are going to fly the Lincoln tomorrow", never having flown a four-engined aircraft before. I can remember very well being introduced to the Lincoln with another pilot, who had also not flown a four-engined aircraft before; we had a QFI with us but no one else, not even an engineer. We went to the aircraft and having got the thing started we taxied out, my colleague in the left-hand seat, the QFI in the right and I was standing between the two. We took off and flew around the local area, the Instructor feathering and un-feathering an engine (just to show how it worked) and came back to the circuit. After two circuits and bumps the QFI got out and left us to work out how to fly a Lincoln! This was very much the attitude and we had some quite exciting times.'

In July the whole Course was stood down for just over a month while the School moved to Farnborough. The Ministry of Education had taken over the College of Aeronautics and bought the whole airfield and it would be inconvenient for ETPS to stay, besides which it had become apparent that there would be increasing competition for accommodation and facilities between the College and the School. There were those, too, who felt that the School would benefit more by returning to an aeronautical testing atmosphere. The School was moved in by August

This doughty old biplane, the Dominie I *HG715*, served with the School for ten years from 1943 to 1953, providing a useful hack aircraft as well as imparting its own idiosyncrasies to the students' repertoire.

and the Course resumed, with a break in the first week of September to visit the SBAC Display at Radlett. The flying was a much busier affair for the students at Farnborough for, instead of having the airfield virtually to themselves, they had to slot in with the RAE's flying programme, which in those days was very heavy; they also had to compete for air space in which to carry out their flying exercises, and get used to the main runway at Farnborough with its approach over the houses and the dip down the middle of the runway. This caused one amusing incident (amongst many others) as Ray Watts recalls:

'We had some flying-boat pilots amongst our students and amongst the School aircraft was one of the late-mark Seafires with Griffon engine and contraprops, a bit of a handful for a chap who was used to four engines and a keel to go into the water. I remember one such on an early solo at Farnborough approaching Runway 25 (the main runway, over the black sheds) and holding off

too high, with the runway falling away from him. He stalled, dropped his starboard wing and by the time he'd caught it he pulled off a reasonable landing at the intersection on to Runway 30!'

Despite the interruptions, No 6 Course managed successfully to complete by the end of the year.

The one civilian test pilot on the Course was Tom Brooke-Smith, who had come from Short's at Rochester where he had been busy testing the flying-boats. He went back there as Chief Test Pilot, going on for years and testing the VTO testbeds built by Short as research aircraft in the sixties. From there he went to Flight Refuelling Ltd, at Tarrant Rushton.

Cranfield was over and ETPS now moved into a more settled existence. Farnborough was to be its home now for twenty years and during those years it had time to develop its potential and adapt to meet the changing patterns of the Aircraft Industry's Research and Development scene.

CHAPTER 4
Farnborough

The move to Farnborough had been a much greater change than simply a move from one base to another. The School had been allocated the buildings occupied from time immemorial by the Royal Air Force's School of Photography, which now moved to Cosford. This accommodation was pleasantly close to the Queen's Hotel at the south-east corner of Farnborough's complex and the buildings were scheduled to be converted and extended. But it was only two years after the end of the war and the building industry, like everything else, was restricted by shortages, quotas and the like. So, when the School arrived at Farnborough in July 1947 it found that both the domestic and technical accommodation was far from ready.

The aircraft were immediately accommodated in the hangars by South Gate which had been used by 4 Squadron's Atlas and Audax aircraft in the 1930s and by the Anti-Aircraft Co-operation Unit during the war. These hangars have since become famous as the 'Black Sheds', being used as a significant reference point for the crowds during the SBAC Displays of the 1950s, '60s and '70s and being historically sited just behind the tree which, legend has it, was where Colonel Cody tethered his first machine for engine runs prior to the first flights of a British-built aircraft. These hangars were about half a mile from the rest of the School, where the technical people were under the aegis still of Maclaren Humphreys, and the actual accommodation for the instructional staff and students was in no way ready. There were fifteen of the former and thirty-two

of the latter; the RAF Mess was in no position to accommodate them, being full itself, so the Commandant, Group Captain Ubee, decided he must seek the help of the Army in Aldershot, the self-styled 'Home of the British Army'. The GOC Aldershot Garrison was sympathetic and offered him the use of Warburg Barracks. It was located in the South Cavalry Area of Aldershot and was a vast early Victorian building, of four storeys, made of grey stone with huge rooms containing high ceilings, cavernous fireplaces and large sash windows. At basement level there was a complete set of stables and some of the rooms had doors wide enough to accommodate horse and rider! Outside was a parade ground surrounded by a high wall and if you kept quiet you could almost hear the clatter of horses' hooves, the jingle of harness and the crunch of cavalry boots!

This was the site on which the PMC had to provide for his forty-seven residents. He managed to engage staff from retired Army officers and people in the Aldershot area who had done similar work for the Army but who had been put out of work by the rundown of the Garrison. In June 1947 Warburg was ready, for the School, to provide bed and breakfast — lunches and evening meals were to be taken in the RAF Canteen. All of this resulted in a degradation from the standard of the Mess at Cranfield and it must have been a shock for the Americans and others from overseas who had not shared the privations of wartime England but, despite the odd grumble, everyone settled in reasonably well. With these privations it was all the more remarkable that No 6 Course finished well and without mishap.

There had been another great change as a result of the move. At Cranfield the School had had its own RAF personnel to carry out all the maintenance and servicing of the aircraft. On moving all the airmen were posted and the ETPS aircraft were placed in the hands of the civilian staff of the Royal Aircraft Establishment at Farnborough who were already hard-pressed. In one respect this meant that the School lost some flexibility, the flexibility which comes from having a Flight Sergeant who says: 'You are to get that done' at any time of day or night as required. But in the long run it had a much greater advantage for, although coming under civilian rules and regulations, the School acquired a maintenance staff who had served RAE during its tremendous wartime expansion, many of whom were ex-RAF anyway and, above all, were used to dealing with a wide variety of aircraft types, including one-off prototypes for which there were no detailed maintenance manuals. They were also accustomed to improvising test installations of equipment and instruments as part of the normal day's work. Thus, where maintaining a fleet of fifteen to twenty different types of aircraft was unusual for RAF personnel, it was 'Situation Normal' for the civilian maintainers at Farnborough and, over the years ahead, a tremendous team was built up on ETPS — the spirit of the School pervading the hangars as well.

All the improvisation, however, was over by the end of 1947 and in December the Staff moved into the new Mess, ready for No 7 Course in the New Year. They liked what they found; the old School of Photography building had been transformed into a small, comfortable Mess which very soon provided that informality and conviviality needed for the type of personnel going through the School. At the western end of the building was the bar (rather like a conservatory added on) which, over the twenty years of occupancy, became a byword for hospitality for aviators, a place where test pilots from all over the world

Formation flying was not part of the Course but was occasionally indulged in. A Lincoln is flanked by a Vampire F 1 and Tempest F 2 over the Bedfordshire countryside near Cranfield on No 7 Course in 1948.

met in friendship, that friendship born of a common task, and common dangers in the ongoing advancement of the aeronautical sciences. There are many who count it a rare privilege to have been members of that unique ETPS Mess at Farnborough between 1948 and 1968.

The Staff for the first all-Farnborough Course was led still by Group Captain Ubee as Commandant, although this would be his last Course, ably assisted by Maclaren Humphreys, who had Mr J. Lawford, BSc, to utilise the new classrooms which, by now, were ready for use. Admin came under a retired officer, Squadron Leader Jones, and the Flying Tutors comprised Flight Lieutenant P. F. Wingate, DFC, Squadron Leader E. Coton, DFC, AFC, Squadron Leader C. B. 'Cyclops' Brown (who also sported a black eye-patch over his right eye), Squadron Leader R. E. Havercroft, AFC, and Flight Lieutenant K. E. Walters, AFC. In addition, there were now other flying personnel allocated due to the increasing number of large aircraft; three Staff Navigators, Flight Lieutenants Glanville, Skilton and Smail and a Staff Signaller, Flying Officer E. C. S. Bradley-Feary, named 'Fred' for short by Flight Lieutenant Pete Wingate and known thus thereafter.

The Aircraft Fleet for this Course was little altered from that which had come from Cranfield and comprised:

1 × Airspeed Oxford T 2
1 × Auster AOP 5
1 × Avro Anson C 19
4 × Avro Lincoln B 2
1 × DH Dominie T 1
1 × DH Mosquito T 3
2 × DH Mosquito B 35
3 × DH Vampire F 1
2 × Fairey Firefly FR 1
2 × Gloster Meteor F 3
1 × Gloster Meteor F 4
2 × Hawker Tempest F 2
3 × North American Harvard
      T 2B

2 × Olympia sailplane
3 × Supermarine Seafire F 46

To these were added, during the Course, another Mosquito T 3, Vampire F 2 and Meteor F 4, and one of the Sea Fury F 10 prototypes, whilst a Seafire F 47 replaced two of the Seafire F 46s and the two Mosquito B 35s departed.

No 7 Course comprised twenty-three students of whom all were from the RAF or RN except for two Canadians and two Americans, one of the latter, Major R. B. Meyersberg, USMC, being from the FAA at Washington.

Everything began to shake down well during this year. Farnborough was enlivened by the addition of this 'youngster' on the station and began to understand the type of flying that the School required. The Mess and new accommodation was soon found to be suitable and the School began to feel the benefit, once more, of operating within a test flying environment where, all around them, they could see the end product of their training taking place by some of their predecessors. So began a process which linked the School firmly with the growing traditions of Farnborough as one of the world's leading centres of aeronautical research. The spin-off for the ETPS was not always quantifiable but it was a very real asset nonetheless.

The Signaller, Eddie Bradley-Feary, had been posted in from 205 Sunderland Squadron, for the purpose of providing additional crew for the Lincolns, this being particularly necessary when pilots unaccustomed to flying twin- or four-engined aircraft were in charge. He remembers:

'Arriving in January 1948, two months before the Course was to start, I was surprised one day when Squadron Leader Havercroft was heard to say "Let's go to Blackpool for lunch". We all piled aboard Lincoln *535* and as Flight Lieutenant Pete Wingate, one of the QFIs, belted down the runway he chanted "With twain did he open the throttles, with twain did he raise the undercart, with twain did he raise the flaps and with twain did he fly" (obviously well acquainted with the sixth chapter of the Prophet Isaiah). I began to wonder just what kind of madhouse I'd come to! At that time the School was unique in having two of the staff sporting black eye-patches as both the Commandant, Group Captain Ubee and Squadron Leader "Cyclops" Brown had lost a right eye in action. "Cyclops" said he always preferred left-hand circuits for that reason. My duty as Signaller was to help crew the Lincolns and I experienced some unconventional moments as singles and twin pilots did a rapid conversion on to them. Some of the exercises later in the Course put the Lincolns through incredible contortions and I still carry memories of diving at high speed with Ben Gunn *standing* in order to put full aileron on in the rate-of-roll tests.

'One or two of the students stand out in memory — Major Bob Meyersberg, USMC, came as a test pilot already to assess the ETPS Course. On one Lincoln trip he decided he wanted to do a bit of sightseeing so we returned to Farnborough across London at 2,000 ft with Bob banking to left and right saying "So that's Buckingham Palace", etc. Lieutenant Dave Morgan, RN, landed a Lincoln as if he was making a carrier landing — most impressive to watch. On two occasions during my time "Balbos" were organised, when all the serviceable aircraft would formate on a specific "target". On No 7 Course this was a "raid" on Boscombe Down, led by Bob Meyersberg, who brought the entire formation back low across Farnborough's 07 runway, getting

lower and lower in the Lincoln until his wingmen were forced to break away. The other one was the following year when Group Captain Snaith walked into the Flight Office and said: "Cranwell are playing the Staff College at Camberley this afternoon" and walked out. In quick time all the available aircraft were organised and the peace of Camberley was shattered by ETPS aircraft formating at low level across Sandhurst's Rugby field. Whether it helped the Cranwell boys or not I never heard.'

The Course was completed on time, marred by one fatal accident in which one of the Canadian students, Squadron Leader C. L. T. Sawle, AFC, was killed in Meteor F 4 *EE568*. Most of its successful members went on to test the new generation of aircraft being developed for the Forces and also some of the revolutionary new test vehicles coming along. Two of this Course were involved with the Boulton Paul Deltas which appeared in the early 'fifties — Squadron Leader Bob Smyth, who returned to 'A' Squadron at Boscombe Down, made the first flight in the P 111 and thereafter AE "Ben" Gunn, who had become Chief Test Pilot for Boulton Paul, went on to do all the development flying on this and its successor, the P 120 from which he had to eject when flying from Boscombe on 29 August 1952. Bob Smyth, after his RAF career, became, until very recently, Chief Test Pilot to Marshall's at Cambridge, supervising the testing of all the types under contract and having been recently responsible for the modifications to the RAF's Hercules to turn them into tankers for the Falklands Campaign. Three others on this Course gave their lives over the following few years, Flight Lieutenant Alston in a Canberra in 1956 and Squadron Leader Roberts in a Gnat in 1959 whilst the USAF officer, Captain Boyd Grubaugh, died in a USAF F-100 Super Sabre in June 1958.

At the end of 1948 Group Captain Ubee stood down, having been responsible for setting up the next stage of ETPS's life at Farnborough. The School could now move forward from the base he had laid. To take it onward came Group Captain L. S. Snaith, AFC. He was another of the old school of test pilots, having been part of the team that clinched the Schneider Trophy for Britain in 1931 and having spent much of his time before and after in testing flying-boats and seaplanes at Felixstowe. When he came to the School he had never flown a jet aircraft, so one of his first acts on coming was to fly a Vampire. On his own admission he got lost on that first jet flight, being caught out by the great increase in speed! Up till now gliding had been part of the Course and available, with the two Olympias, for all the students but Snaith pushed this enthusiastically and there was a surge forward in the gliding activities of the School, so much so that one of the students on the next course, Bill Bedford, established a record on one of his first few flights.

The new Course was bigger, with thirty students, being more international again with an Australian, two Canadians, two Indians and two from the US Navy. A new Chief Ground Instructor, G. W. Jones was understudying Maclaren Humphreys, whose last year with the School this was to be. The fleet was increased, too, to cope with the bigger numbers but, apart from the addition of one of the new de Havilland Devons, the additions were just more of the types already in the fleet.

One of Snaith's new ideas was the Crest. He thought it was ridiculous that the School did not have its own armorial bearings and set about remedying this. It was discussed at a fairly high level in the Ministry and approved. Money was set aside for this and the Chester College of Heralds commissioned to design it. Maclaren Humphreys was in on this and he commented:

'While they were busy designing the Crest the question of a suitable motto arose and I suggested "Learn to Test — Test to Learn"; I thought it would make a good Latin tag because things like that quite often do come out well in Latin. When it went up to the College of Heralds they thought it would be better left in English.' And so it has remained.

'Azure semée of Mullets Or on a Pale Argent, a Torch enflamed proper. And for the Crest Issuant from an Astral Crown Or an Eagle wings elevated and addorsed Azure.'

Group Captain Snaith recalls:

'In connection with the presentation of armorial bearings, I thought it would be a good idea for the Chief of the Air Staff, Lord Tedder, to come. I knew him well, having served under him many years ago. Well, he said he certainly would come and pulling my leg he sent me "battle orders", which started off like this — "Group Captain Snaith will be in Command of the RAF Regiment at 10 o'clock, at five minutes past ten Lord Tedder will arrive on horseback, supported admirably by a number of troops. Group Captain Snaith will bring the parade to attention and will conduct Lord Tedder to the Dais" — and he went on like this, really as a leg pull. To my astonishment I found it down in the brochure that this actually happened. Well, it didn't, it was just a leg pull by Lord Tedder who was full of fun actually — although some people didn't realise. He did come to the dinner where the armorial bearings were presented.'

In the late 1940s and early '50s the aircraft industries of the world faced tremendous challenges. The jet engine had provided whole new parameters of flight

In December 1949 the School was presented with its Armorial Bearings, and was afterwards addressed by Marshal of the Royal Air Force, Lord Tedder, seen here at the ensuing Dinner, just behind the McKenna Trophy. The Commandant at the time was Group Captain L. S. Snaith, AFC, who is looking somewhat pensive behind the carnations.

beyond previous limits and into realms unknown, principally the supersonic hurdle. So the accent in the test pilot training of the time had to be on performance testing of aircraft engines. Within a few years no fewer than ten of No 8 Course had been killed in the development programmes within the Western world — Lieutenant Orr-Ewing in an Attacker the following year; Lieutenant Commander Weems, US Navy, in 1951; Flight Lieutenant B. Warre, RCAF, in the development of the Avro Canada CF-100 fighter in 1951; and so it goes on, Flight Lieutenant Bradwell, Lieutenant Cawood, Flight Lieutenant Clark, Squadron Leader Cleaver, Captain Davis, USAF, Squadron Leader Ecclestone and Lieutenant Robertson, RN.

One of the Indians, Flight Lieutenant S. Das, went on to reach Group Captain in the Indian Air Force and followed this with a distinguished career as Chief Test Pilot of Hindustan Aircraft in Bangalore, being killed eventually while testing the indigenous HF 24 Marut fighter. Bill Bedford, who had taken to gliding so wholeheartedly on the Course, returned immediately in 1950 as a tutor on the next course and then began a career with Hawker Siddeley which took him to the forefront of technological development, flying with the Vertical Take-off and Landing P1127, Kestrel and Harrier with which his name will always be associated. Jimmy Harrison went into the same company, after a period of service test flying and rose to be Chief Test Pilot of what was then Avro and became the Manchester Division of Hawker Siddeley and is now British Aerospace, during which time he was involved in Shackleton, Vulcan, HS 748 and Nimrod programmes. He recollects:

'In 1949 I suppose things were not done in quite the same way that they would be nowadays. There was a tendency to give one of the students a set of pilots' notes and the aeroplane and he was expected to go up and do his bit — which seemed to work in general terms. I suppose there were some narrow squeaks. In my case I had never flown a jet aeroplane. Nobody had ever told me they used a lot of fuel at low altitude and the first modest little task I was given was a cockpit assessment in a Meteor 4. I went and assessed the cockpit for half an hour, thought it was time to go home. How does one get back over 10/10ths cloud — well obviously one drops below the cloud and finds one's way home. I was in the middle of the Channel as it turned out and passing Tangmere I realised with about 20/20 on the clock that I ought really to be landing to refuel but I could hardly do this on my first ever flight on ETPS, so I reckoned I'd make it.

'Passing the Hog's Back I was beginning to get fairly nervous and I had to call in for a straight approach — both fuel gauges were reading 0/0 at this time, both engines flamed out as I landed on the runway. The Chief Flying Instructor, as I recall, wasn't a bit angry about running out of fuel but he asked if I had switched off the booster pumps when I ran out because if I hadn't I would have rogered the pumps — they would be dry having no fuel to work. That was all that was ever said. Anyway I learnt a lesson that jet aeroplanes do use a lot of fuel at low altitude. It wasn't quite all as disastrous as that, I managed to pass with a special distinction and I suppose that took me to Aero Flight.

'The technical instruction at ETPS in those days was absolutely first class because we had the good fortune to have MH for at least half of our course. If I had any criticism at all it would be that there was a tendency for the technician, or the scientist as he would prefer to be called, to over-emphasise the thought that it was for the pilot to describe what he did and what had happened, and it was for the "scientist" to decide what to do about it. Once one gets into industry it is a far cry from that sort of situation. Later on one discovers that having built up a good relationship between the Chief Test Pilot and the Chief Designer, certainly in the first few months of development flying, it is for the Chief Test Pilot to say what is unacceptable, and for the Chief Designer and his staff to get it right.'

Ted Tennant went on with Service test flying and then joined Folland to test Petter's range of lightweight fighters and trainers, the Midge and Gnat, with which he had his share of excitements.

Mention has already been made of the visits to the industry which punctuated the Course, providing relaxing highlights in the otherwise hard work of the year's activities. Group Captain Snaith went one better than this, taking them all — students and staff — off to Naples where they joined the USS *Coral Sea* and spent a week at sea on Mediterranean exercises, watching the Carrier Air Group in action. A link was forged with the ship and a copy of the ETPS armorial bearings hangs to this day in the ship's Wardroom.

As the School moved into the 1950s Snaith was still in command for No 9 Course with Commander P. S. Wilson as his Chief Test Flying Instructor and Jones now having taken over from 'Humph' as Chief Ground Instructor, backed up by L. R. Jenkins. The 'other Jones' remained as Adjutant and Tutors comprised Squadron Leader R. F. 'Dicky' Martin, DFC, AFC, Squadron Leader C. K. Saxelby, DFC, and Flight Lieutenant A. W. (Bill) Bedford, AFC. There were some changes in the types in the fleet with the Tempests and

The move to Farnborough had brought ETPS back into the test flying world once more. Its accommodation, the old School of Photography, was next to the Queen's Hotel (the castle-like building in the background of the picture) and comprised the instructional blocks in the foreground and the famous ETPS Mess behind.

Seafires disappearing and the Valetta transport and Avro Athena joining the School, whose aircraft were now housed just down the hill from the Mess in 'E' Shed beside the road from the Queen's to the Golf Course at Farnborough. The Athena was an interesting aircraft to have; it had been a competitor with the Boulton Paul Balliol as the new basic trainer for the RAF, first as a turboprop trainer. The RAF then had second thoughts and asked them to be re-engined with Rolls-Royce Merlin engines. Seventeen pre-production aircraft were built of each type and the Balliol eventually won the contract so the seventeen Athenas were spare. Some went to the RAF College at Cranwell and three came to ETPS where they had the advantage, for the students, of being a type they had never seen or flown before. Such a

type, for which there were no comprehensive manuals and little experience of maintaining, could have presented problems but to Farnborough's ground crews new and unusual types were the norm.

Course No 9 again had much the same mix as the previous ones except there were no students from the Indian sub-continent. Four Americans, three Canadians and an Australian made up the contribution from outside the RAF and RN. Unfortunately the RAAF member, Squadron Leader C. W. Stark, AFC, was killed on the Course in Vampire F 1 *TG388* on 13 April. Another Course member, Lieutenant W. N. Plews, RN, was killed in an accident in an Avro Lincoln before the year was out. Several of this Course went on to serve with the aircraft manufacturing firms in the UK: J. W. Allam to Handley Page, becoming

Chief Test Pilot at Radlett until the company's demise; W. R. 'Jeep' Gellatly became one of the country's first helicopter test pilots and rose to become Chief Test Pilot at Westland during his career there. Lieutenant S. B. Oliver went into BAC and then on into the airline business; Walter Runciman, a New Zealander, went to Short's after ETPS and flew the unconventional Sherpa movable-wing glider, the Sperrin four-jet bomber and the Seamew and it was in one of these that he was killed at Sydenham airfield on 9 June 1956. Flight Lieutenant L. M. Whittington went on from his RAF test career, in which he was awarded an AFC, to Hawker at Dunsfold.

Gliding remained one of the most active and recreative of the School's pursuits and the Auster AOP VF627 was kept busy towing the Olympias down to Chilbolton airfield on Salisbury Plain, from where all the gliding was performed, and then back again.

By now the techniques of test pilot training had been steadily refined at Farn-borough and nowhere was this refinement more noticeable than in the syndicate system. At the beginning of No 7 Course Squadron Leader Havercroft, who was now OC Flying, Squadron Leader E. Coton and 'Cyclops' Brown got together and, to improve the quality of the training, worked out this new system. There had already been some dissatisfaction expressed during the courses at Cranfield that the student population was not getting value for money out of the tutors, the main problems being that the students did not have one fixed tutor to whom they were allocated for advice and guidance, not only on the flying but on all aspects of the Course. There was another 'beef' that, too often, the students were just given Pilots' Notes on a new type and told to go and fly it but had never had any adequate in-flight instruction on test flying techniques.

Brown, Coton and Havercroft set about establishing a method whereby these problems could be identified and remedied. In establishing the syndicate system the students were grouped into three syndi-

Amongst the more interesting types that the students flew in the early 1950s were the prototype turboprop trainers, the Avro Athens and Boulton Paul Balliol. Undergoing servicing at Farnborough is VL892, one of the prototype Balliols, which served with ETPS in 1952-53.

Gliding had been introduced early on at ETPS, not simply as a recreation but as a means of extending the students' aeronautical experience as well as giving them some well-earned relaxation. This evening scene shows instructor and pupil walking out to Singsby Sedbergh *WB920* from the Farnborough flight offices down in Dingley Dell (now part of the civil enclave there).

cates, originally broken down by past flying experience, ie, all bomber pilots in one, all fighter pilots in another and all training/transport chaps in a third. This cut across nationalities and air arms but it did mean that any flying problems which came up would tend to be problems common to all the members of the syndicate by virtue of their past experience. For example, all the ex-bomber pilots would tend to find the same difficulties when first tackling a Spitfire, etc. Each syndicate would be given a syndicate leader whose duty it was to feel the pulse of his men and report any difficulties within the syndicate to the syndicate tutor. Thus, each tutor now dealt with a specific number of students with whom he could specialise and whom he could get to know better than when his duties were spread across the whole course.

Similarly, to counter the lack of airborne

instructional flying certain aircraft were used purely for demonstration work. An aircraft like the Oxford could get airborne with more than one student aboard and the tutor could demonstrate flying characteristics and the testing techniques needed to obtain the necessary data for test purposes. In short, they were used as flying classrooms. Obviously the bigger aircraft were better for this and this has since been a useful feature of the transport type aircraft that the School's fleet has had.

These innovations had been planned for No 7 Course but, due to the upheavals with the move, accommodation problems and the initial shortage of maintenance staff, the flying programme had got so far behind during the Course that it was not really until No 8 Course that the full benefits of these instructions became manifest.

Refinements were made to the syndicate

system as time went on but it has remained the bedrock of the School's methods ever since.

Let Wing Commander Robin Hargreaves, ETPS's Commanding Officer in the early 1980s, describe the system as it still applies today.

'The core of our teaching system at ETPS is the student syndicate — that is a small group of three or, at the most, four students and one flying tutor. It is a tutorial system just as is used at Oxbridge and the way we work this at ETPS is that the team of students will be attached to a given tutor for the first term at the School, for the second term they will move on to another tutor and for the third term to the third tutor. Now what all this does is to expose them to each of these tutor's very different backgrounds and test experiences, so that

at the end of the year they have the benefit of three different individual experiences of test flying. It is also a very powerful teaching method because it is very close — not one-to-one but one-to-three or -four — so that the interchange between the tutor and the students is immediate, effective and personal. The tutors get to know the students extremely well and vice versa so that a student's strengths and weaknesses become apparent very quickly, and he can give particular attention to those areas where he is weakest and his particular virtues will be recognised early on. It really is very different from a classroom system. The syndicate will go through a period of three months working together, briefing, flying together, debriefing a report and at the end of that three months

One of the factors of the ETPS course which appalled most students was the sheer amount of study and report writing that was involved. This was done either in one's quarters or in the ETPS Library, as is being done by these members of No 19 Course in July 1960. They are Lieutenant J. A. Carrodous, RN, and Lieutenant E. J. Hogan, US Navy, on the left and Flight Lieutenants I. H. Keppie and G. T. Cannon on the right.

they really know each other extremely well.

'In the next term they move on to another tutor — he might be an American so trained at a different school, flown different aeroplanes, a different approach to testing, but basically doing the same job — so this is the way, in a paradoxical sort of method, we standardise the style. We do not attempt to standardise the actual instruction — that would be impossible and in any case would not be good. We say that what the student needs to get is the full range of backgrounds and experiences which is far more valuable to them than any set piece training system — we do not say "Here is a set of objectives, when you have learned these you are a test pilot". Our training is open-ended — what we are trying to do is to get the best out of the best people and an acceptable standard out of the less than best so that everybody reaches what we regard as a minimum acceptable standard, but the top few will achieve much better than that. In other words, it is an unashamedly elitist style of training.'

From then on ETPS was set fair for the first half of the 1950s. With No 10 Course (1951) there were changes in the staff. Group Captain A. E. Clouston, DSO, DFC, AFC, took over as Commandant; he came with a tremendous record in the aviation world. He had been a Farnborough test pilot during the war, having taken part in some very hazardous tests at the beginning of the war (one being to fly aircraft deliberately into barrage balloon cables to see how effective these were), he had taken part in long-distance record attempts in the 1930s and had played a significant role in the operational war against the U-boat, commanding No 224

(Liberator) Squadron in 1943-44. This New Zealander now came to command for the next three years.

Wing Commander E. N. M. Sparks, who had been on 5 Course as a Squadron Leader at Cranfield, had already taken over as the CTFI in 1950 and P. L. Bisgood came in as Chief Ground Instructor. There were three new Tutors, all ETPS graduates, Lieutenant Commander Ken Hickson, Squadron Leader G. Banner, DFC, and Squadron Leader W. J. Sheehan, DFC. The Course itself comprised twenty-seven students; four from the United States (two USAF, two US Navy), an Australian (RAAF), Canadian and an Indian, as well as four from the Royal Navy and the rest from the RAF. One of the latter, however, withdrew from the Course.

There was one fatility approximately halfway through the Course when Flight Lieutenant R. B. Connell, DFC, was killed in a Sea Fury crash on 12 July. Many of this Course went into the heavy programme of experimental flying, both in the UK and in their own countries and paid a heavy price, no fewer than seven being killed before the decade was out. The two US Navy men went back into higher positions within the Navy; Lieutenant P. M. 'Sheepy' Lamb found a novel test flying role in joining the British Hovercraft Corporation and becoming their Chief Test Pilot, developing their range of products from Cowes in the Isle of Wight and never flying more than a few inches above ground level! Squadron Leader W. J. Potocki, DFC, joined Avro Canada and became their Chief Test Pilot, transferring to North American Rockwell when the CF-105 was cancelled. Lieutenant W. H. Sear, RN, concentrated on helicopter development flying and eventually became a key man at Westland at Yeovil, taking over eventually as Manager, Flight Operations. Another graduate of this Course also moved into the then new field of helicoptering; this was Flight Lieutenant

J. K. Hough, AFC, the Course's McKenna Trophy Winner. As one of the few serving as a test pilot at Farnborough on helicoptering, he was killed in a Bristol Sycamore there on 8 September 1953. Flight Lieutenant Roger Topp served in the test world for a while then, in January 1955, took command of Treble-One Squadron, a Hunter squadron at North Weald. He fashioned a formation aerobatic team there which two years later expanded into the Black Arrows, the official RAF formation aerobatic team, with shiny black Hunter F 6s which set a new standard of artistry in formation aerobatics. Reinforced with aircraft from other squadrons he flew a 22-ship formation and performed a roll with this large, unwieldy formation, the greatest number before or since. The Squadron continued in this field for several years, setting the standard carried on since by the Red Arrows. He later returned to the test flying world, becoming the Commandant of the A&AEE, Boscombe Down, at the beginning of the 1970s

The only new type to join the School for this Course was the de Havilland Canada Chipmunk, which became instantly popular, and was thrown into the glider towing task as well as being used for performance assessment. A later student, Flight Lieutenant A. M. Christie, now Group Captain, said of the Chipmunk in ETPS:

'I found it quite fascinating flying the Chipmunk on occasions because during assessment of spinning trials you did the Chipmunk at aft CG and that was interesting. At aft CG it went flat very quickly and took a few turns before coming out. Playing back the wire recorder (used to record the student's voice for playback and assessment purposes) after you had been climbing up and doing a series of such spins it became quite a problem sorting out what you were actually saying on it. Counting the number of turns in a flat spin on the Chipmunk was quite difficult and I remember I used to go over to the Hog's Back where you had this long straight line of hills, with a main road, the A31, on it, and you could watch every time the road passed by.'

For Course 11 in 1952 further aircraft types arrived. Particularly helpful was the Gloster Meteor T 7, the two-seater trainer version, which gave great scope for jet test techniques to be demonstrated by tutors at last. On the 'heavy' side came the Vickers Valetta and Varsity, two aircraft from the same stable and basically Wellington developments but very different to fly. The Varsity was a real 'lady' of an aircraft with no adverse characteristics, even on one engine. By contrast the Valetta, military version of the Viking airliner, could be, to quote one of the students, 'a real cow on one engine'. It was on one of the latter, *VL266*, that the only fatilities on the Course took place, on 19 August when it crashed near Odiham killing the Australian, Flight Lieutenant M. Marcovitch and Flight Lieutenant L. H. Wilkinson. The Course comprised thirty-four students, four Americans and one Indian besides the two mentioned above, all the rest being RAF and RN. Major Joe Cotton of the USAF went on to test the advanced bombers that were later developed for the USAF, specifically the B-58 and B-70. Another new name, this time on the staff, was a Flight Lieutenant P. W. Stevens who came to the School to look after the administrative side of things. As we shall see, he played a large part in the School's affairs in years to come.

Commander Ken R. Hickson of the Royal Navy had taken the Chief Test Flying Instructor's position which he held for two years, becoming OC Flying at the RAE Bedford in the 1960s. He continued as CTFI for No 12 Course in 1953 alongside

Group Captain Clouston who relinquished the task in the course of the year to none other than one who had played such a large part in the original formation of ETPS at Boscombe Down, Group Captain Sammy Wroath. Not only did he take up the reins of the School once more but stayed for four years, seeing it through the mid-1950s. As well as the normal task of being godfather to the students and administering the courses Wroath had a specific duty to perform. The Ministry were already looking askance at the costs the School was running up. There have always been those who thought that ETPS was an expensive luxury and as the costs went up it simply added fuel to their ideas that perhaps the RAF could do without it.

As Wroath himself says:

'It is not so difficult to understand that once you introduce flying on to a course where aeroplanes are estimated to cost hundreds of pounds an hour it doesn't take very long to run up a monumental bill and this was particularly so in the case of the foreign students who paid then £6,000 per course — whereas it literally cost between £50,000 and £60,000 because of the large amount of flying they had done. So my task was to re-vamp the syllabus in such a way that we could cover the whole of the tests with the minimum number of hours (we found, for example, that some of the students got 300 hours, some only 200 hours). By re-vamping the syllabus we came up with something like 105/110 hours; we also re-planned the fleet usage so that we used the cheaper aeroplanes for the first part of the Course. As a result the cost of running the School was very much reduced and that made me pretty popular with the Ministry. I think we saved about half-a-million pounds and the Ministry gave me half of it

back again so that I was able to buy a new Canberra and Hunter with the money.'

The flying hours above appear to have been drastically reduced but in many ways they could be cut logically. For example, many of the routine tests had been flown in a straight line and as a result students on the faster aircraft would find themselves, say, in Cornwall at the end of the test; they then had 200 miles of back-tracking to do. With the test flights replanned they could be flown so that the same test could be done but the flight end up within a few miles of the airfield. It was another example of being methodical and this was one of the attributes the students were supposed to be learning anyway.

One of the problems that Group Captain Wroath encountered was in part a result of the re-equipment programme that the RAF was experiencing from 1953 onwards. Both Bomber Command and Fighter Command were introducing new advanced types of aircraft from the mid-1950s (the V-Bombers and the transonic fighters); they were therefore very loath to part with their good pilots even though they had volunteered.

Wroath says:

'The Commander in Chief of Fighter Command wrote a little note on the top of some applications saying "We are not going to part with him". When this C-in-C became Chief of Air Staff he once stopped me in the road and said he couldn't understand why there weren't many fighter pilots at Boscombe Down testing these new aircraft and I replied that the reason was simply because chaps like him had stopped them.'

The post of Chief Ground Instructor was taken over by H. W. Turner with L. R. Jenkins still there to assist him. New tutors comprised two Squadron Leaders from No 9 Course, C. H. Macfie and D. J.

Murphy, both had DFCs. The Course itself comprised twenty-four students of whom nine came from overseas — a Swede, four Americans, a Frenchman, a Canadian, an Italian and an Australian, Unusually, there was a civilian from the British Aviation industry, Mr R. V. Morris from the Fairey Aviation Co. There was only one fatility on 12 Course, US Navy Lieutenant Commander A. C. Koplewski, who was killed flying a Westland Wyvern, an aircraft that had killed others before him. However, within two years four more had been killed, three in test flying; these were Captain P. W. Bryce, USAF, who was killed in a Northrop F-89 Scorpion, Captain B. O. J. Fryklund, the Swede, who was killed in 1954 in a SAAB Lansen and Lieutenant Commander T. A. Rickell, RN, killed flying one of the Supermarine 525s, *VX138*, whilst on test from Boscombe Down on 5 July 1955.

The following year (1954) saw an increased number of students forming No 13 Course. This again was a wide-ranging course with overseas representatives making up fourteen members, from Australia, America, Norway, Thailand, Italy, France, Canada and the Netherlands. There were changes in the staff, too. Wing Commander K. J. Sewell, AFC, DFM, one of the original students on No 1 Course, returned after a distinguished career to become CTFI, whilst J. A. Lang took over from Mr Turner as Chief Ground Instructor. One of the new Flying Tutors was Squadron Leader A. E. Marriott who had been on No 4 Course. The strictly male establishment at ETPS was invaded by Mrs M. Willcocks who came in to assist J. A. Lang with the ground instruction.

The School had taken on board three new types in 1953 which came into their own for 13 Course; now that the RAF had two-seat Vampire trainers, a couple of these were added to the fleet as part of the economy campaign, being economical jet trainers. On the piston side had come the Hunting-Percival Provost which proved a very useful tool, whilst a Hastings was added to the 'heavies' to give a slightly more up-to-date machine than the wartime Lincolns.

This Course passed through completely free of fatal accidents, a heartening testimony to the improvements that had been brought into the syllabus and training. The students went out far and wide from this course. Captain R. Bignamini returned to the Italian Air Force for test flying duties then left the service to become Chief Test Pilot for Fiat at Caselle. Flight Lieutenant B. Sukhanusasna took the skills he had learned back to Thailand and the Royal Thai Air Force. Flight Lieutenant J. G. Burns, Lieutenant D. J. Whitehead and Lieutenant G. R. Higgs all went on to test careers in the Ministry of Supply establishments, then met up at Hawker Siddeley at Brough where they were heavily committed to the development and production of the Buccaneer, Derek Whitehead becoming Chief Test Pilot at the company's airfield at Holme-on-Spalding Moor and undertaking the major part of the development flying on the Buccaneer. Higgs, who made the headlines by flying a Buccaneer S 2 back from Goose Bay to Lossiemouth without refuelling in 1965 to prove that the S Mk 2, unlike the S Mk 1, had ample range in its tanks, later took command of the RAE's test airfield at Thurleigh, Bedford. Captain Ivan Kincheloe, USAF, who went on to be an enormously effective and popular test pilot at Edwards Air Force Base until he was killed in an F-104 in 1958, succeeded in writing off several of the School's aircraft during the Course, including the Sedbergh glider, a Devon and a Sea Fury, the latter by dropping an undercarriage leg down a rabbit hole doing take-off and landing assessments at Chilbolton (Brer Rabbit 1: ETPS Nil).

One of the problems that has always afflicted ETPS has been the fact that the aircraft in its fleet were always way behind the type of machine the students would be flying for real and this disparity became greater at the time of the mid-1950s when great advances in aerodynamics and design were being translated into actual hardware and into production, with the result that squadron pilots were very often flying more advanced airframes than the budding test pilots! The 1954 Course was a case in point because, although the Hunter was now established in RAF service, no examples were to be seen on the School's flight line. Another problem was the handling of turboprop engines. These were in service both with the Navy and the airlines yet there were none for ETPS. By and large it was a money problem, for brand-new aeroplanes were outside the School's budget; we have already mentioned how Sammy Wroath acquired a Canberra and Hunter (in 1955) by stringent cost cutting. Another solution presented itself to the Ministry and on face value it looked an even better idea. Why not give ETPS actual prototype aircraft for which the Ministry had no further use? Not only would they be more up-to-date but they would almost certainly have interesting flying characteristics as they were raw, rather than refined aircraft. Accordingly, one of the first such aircraft arrived in 1954 to overcome the lack of turboprop experience.

The aircraft concerned was the second prototype Armstrong Whitworth Apollo, a four-engined airliner which was built in competition with the Vickers Viscount. The latter won the orders for BEA and other airlines so further development of the Apollo was abandoned. Equipped with four Armstrong Siddeley Mamba turboprops, the Apollo also gave students some idea of a modern civil airliner (more modern than the Hastings). It arrived in March 1954 and although the School endeavoured to use it, it was too much of a one-off and temperamental headache to be of much use as a flying machine. At the end of the Course it was transferred to the RAE as a ground static structural test vehicle.

Getting on the Course was not always easy for serving pilots. Commanding Officers obviously wanted to retain their good pilots. Flight Lieutenant A. M. Christie's experience was just one:

'My application for the Empire Test Pilots' School was made out in Iraq. I was a member of No 6 Squadron flying Venoms. My Squadron Commander was Squadron Leader Red Roberts, quite a well known test pilot, who unfortunately was killed at Boscombe Down after he had come back and, I think, become senior pilot on "A" Squadron. Red Roberts, when he knew I was interested in test flying, said "All right, I am willing to recommend you". Being in Iraq it was awkward and difficult for me to come back to do all the necessary interviews — in any case I was being shuttled around in the Middle East. I became CO of Sharjah for a little while before I came back to 6 Squadron. I think on Red Roberts' recommendation, and to some extent Sammy Wroath's, I was accepted for ETPS. When I arrived at Farnborough Sammy Wroath, who was Commandant, told me they had taken me a bit on spec on the basis of Red Roberts' recommendation. So, in fact, I was accepted for ETPS to do the course in 1955 basically through the back door. It was unusual to get a guy going in that way and so from our point of view I think perhaps I was unique in some respects. I think many of the Commonwealth candidates had to make the journey to the UK to be selected and the foreigners, because they paid for the course, were selected in their own countries.'

The year 1955 saw No 14 Course almost

over-subscribed, eventually working out at thirty-nine students. Two Italians, a Dutchman, a French sailor, an Egyptian and a Swede came from Europe whilst the Commonwealth provided three Australians and four Canadians, one, Mr W. Gadzes, a civilian, and the American forces provided three. The Staff added three new tutors, Squadron Leader A. W. Johnson, DFC, S. J. Hubbard, DFC, AFC, and Lieutenant Commander C. E. Price, all graduates of previous courses, Sadly, the CTFI, Wing Commander K. J. 'Pock' Sewell, AFC, DFM, was killed during the Course in the School's Pembroke *WV698*. On 11 May 1955 it had an engine fire and crashed between Andover and Boscombe Down. This was a blow indeed, but his place was taken almost immediately by Wing Commander I. N. M. Macdonald, AFC, who had been a student on 7 Course.

It was on this Course that the advent of more modern aircraft began to be felt, with both Canberras and Hunters being available. Another of the 'tired prototypes' relegated to ETPS was the one and only Avro 707B. This was a most valuable aircraft, being a miniature Vulcan with interesting delta characteristics, of which more anon.

Another of the methods of cutting down expensive flying hours that ETPS employed was to send students away for conversion courses before starting in on the Course itself. Thus Flight Lieutenant (now Group Captain) A. M. Christie, who had arrived from 6 Squadron in Iraq, flying Venoms, went to the AFS at Swinderby to convert to heavy twins. The type he flew was the Varsity which gave him a gentleman's eye view of twins, and in no way prepared him for the School's Valettas. The Valetta must have been a real problem — Christie recalls that the expert on it was one of the instrument rating examiners, a chap called Jack Hindle, whose great demonstration was to take off and very quickly throttle back an engine, quickly come round down-

wind at about 500-600 ft (150-180m) then swing round and do a single-engined landing. Then he would say 'Right, you do it' and you would take off on two, he would throttle one back at the same point and you would struggle for ages to hold the thing straight, pick up speed, get the wheels up and generally get the thing into a controllable condition by which time you had wandered for miles and miles across the Hampshire countryside before anything seemed under control.

Reggie Spiers, another student on 14 Course said of the Valetta:

'It was like landing an aeroplane with two pogo sticks on the undercarriage, on the end of which were fitted a couple of balloons. Very few people, including Peter Bardon, who had about three and a half thousand hours on it, could really land it consistently on three points.'

Christie mentioned that, compared with an operational squadron, he was surprised at the small amount of flying done on the Course, about 100 hours, but what was done was very concentrated in that you had to work and get information going all the time using knee pads and the wire recorder after which all this information had to be put in a report, probably in the evenings, and the reports counted for a lot with the staff.

'I went to the Course with anticipation of all sorts of exciting new type flying and I wasn't disappointed. I mean exciting in the sense of getting a world of flying opening up in terms of flying different sizes, without having to worry about all the necessary rules and regulations of being qualified on type. You were taught a basic approach to flying a new type which was really marvellous so that it didn't matter whether one flight you were flying a light single-engined jet and the next a multi-engined piston aircraft.

'Someone who springs to mind on the course is Giovanni Franchini (now a General), the Italian. He used to regale us with great stories of being shot down numerous times by Spitfires. When we went to the firms — Supermarine, Vickers and Hawkers — we were allowed to fly some of their older aeroplanes. The foreigners were given first choice of the Spitfire and Hurricane and Franchini's great enjoyment during the course, probably the highlight of the course as far as he was concerned, was to fly the Spitfire — because he had been shot down by Spitfires so often during the war. Then there was the other Italian, Mike Colagiovanni. He became a General as well. He arrived on the course with very basic English spoken, unable to write English, but by the end of the course he was writing all his reports in English. It was a great difficulty to be in — he would write out everything in Italian and translate it into English — laboriously translate it himself. His was a great achievement but he is very intelligent. He went on to be the Italian Air Force's Mr MRCA.'

Reggie Spiers also went to the Course with a basically fighter background and went on a twin conversion course, this time at Stradishall on the Valetta and he, too, was delighted with the variety of types and the trust that was placed in the students. He remembers:

'I can recall going off in a Canberra, still thumbing through the Pilots' Notes to find out what the speed over the hedge was.' He also comments of the heavier aircraft that the physical effort of flying in them was enormous because you were usually divided up into crews of two, one of whom spent the time humping vast bags of lead shot from front end to back end to vary the centre of gravity.

The Hunter F 1 which Sammy Wroath had acquired with his savings was the pride of the fleet. However, Spiers reveals that it really suffered defects in a lot of its systems:

'The "dolls eyes" (hydraulic pressure gauges) never seemed to work and most of us took off with either or both unserviceable. I shudder to think, looking back on it, that we actually did this sort of thing.'

However, the Hunter was no match for the Egyptian student on the course, Squadron Leader F. Zaher. Group Captain Christie describes him as 'a Farouk type, big and heavily built who was terribly well paid and spent much of his spare time in London. He was an outstanding pilot but did not seem to have his heart in the Course.' Anyhow, on 18 July he went off in the Hunter for handling assessments at high indicated airspeed which involved flying down to the South Coast, flying at very high power and speed until the readings were taken, and then return. He had taken off clean, ie, with no external fuel tanks and the Hunter F 1 was notoriously low on internal fuel. On his return he flew a practice GCA and elected to roll and do a visual circuit as well and on his way round the fuel gave out and he plummeted into the ground in Cove, just by the married quarters in Beverly Crescent. He died on his way to the Cambridge Military Hospital in Aldershot.

Another 'used-up' prototype which came ETPS's way in 1955 was the Avro 707B. This was a most useful tool for it was a small scale Vulcan

One of the long-standing tools of the School was the Gloster Meteor, in its various forms, from the early F Mk 3 through to the NF Mk 14. With its two engines placed well out on the wings it provided testing assymetric qualities for the students. *WH312* is a Mark 8 and served at Farnborough during the early fifties.

bomber and exhibited all the idiosyncrasies of a high performance delta aircraft. Reggie Spiers calls it 'a fiendish little single-seater with a strange set of characteristics including a nose-down trim change on putting the airbrakes out which required a one hundred pound pull force on the stick to stop the aircraft from going downhill. It had no anti-surge baffles in the wing tanks and the fuel used to slosh about, adding another dimension to the already quite wobbly lateral and directional characteristics. The ground effect was quite spectacular — when you got near the ground you got a very marked trim change nose up which tended to make you climb so you had to stick the nose down and as soon as you got back into the ground effect up it went again so you went in a series of divergent oscillations until the speed dropped off and you landed.'

Of the chaps on the Course, a number went on to do well in the test flying field. Reggie Spiers himself became CTFI at ETPS in 1968, then became CO Experimental Flying at Farnborough and finally Comman-

dant at Boscombe Down from which he retired. Captain Jack Allavie, USAF, went back to Edwards Air Force Base where he flew the B-52s which launched the X-1 and other hypersonic and sub-stratospheric aircraft, eventually leaving the USAF and serving with McDonnell Douglas as a test pilot at Long Beach.

Ken Murray, the Australian was quite a character. He came to the School with a DFC, AFC and DFM on his tunic, having served with No 77 Squadron, RAAF, in the Korean War. As Group Captain Christie recalls:

'His great claim to fame on 77 Squadron was that he shot down a MiG-15 using his air-to-ground rockets. During an operational sortie the Squadron was bounced by MiGs — two aircraft overshot the Meteors and he took a shot at them with his rockets and claimed to have shot down one of them.' On his return he served with the RAAF Aircraft Research and Development Unit at Laverton.

The 1950s were the heydays for the School's visits to industry. The firms were extremely hospitable and generous and, according to Spiers, they also allowed you to fly their aeroplanes, a thing that seems impossible today. There were also more firms in existence in those days. An example was the trip to Hawker: the day was spent at Dunsfold flying the Tomtit, Hart and Hurricane. The Frenchman, 1st Lieutenant D. L. P. de Lavergne, put up a black by flying off in the Tomtit for an hour and a half! After lunch the party would move off to Langley to look round the factory there, 'and then we all climbed aboard a pleasure cruiser and sailed up the river to Skindles, where they gave us a first class banquet in the evening and put us up for the night'.

Group Captain Christie was most impressed on flying the Hawker Hart.

> 'It was interesting in many respects in that it had an all-flying tail which is unusual. This was a great "new" aerodynamic feature of the aircraft of the 'fifties and 'sixties and here was a biplane of pre-war vintage with the same device. It was very heavy on the controls but responsive.'

At the end of the Course Lieutenant Bob Moore of the US Navy took the coveted McKenna Trophy. And with the Trophy presented at the McKenna Dinner the Course ran down, the graduates departed and the staff began to prepare for No 15 Course. The team had the same staff, Wroath, Macdonald and Lang and no new tutors and Flight Lieutenant P. W. Stevens had arrived to begin his long reign as School Adjutant.

No 15 Course was of more manageable proportions with thirty-two students. Four were Canadians, three Air Force and one Navy, two Indians, three Americans (one USAF, two US Navy), two Italians, two Australians, one Belgian and one Swede. The rest were from the RAF and RN. In fact this Course proceeded very similarly to the previous one, the staff having established a satisfactory basis and the fleet remaining very similar. A Fairey Gannet arrived for this Course, giving valuable turboprop experience, and the Avro 707B finally bit the dust when one of the students could not get the better of its weird landing idiosyncrasies and cartwheeled across the grass at Farnborough.

The Course provided a rich source of ongoing test pilots for the Services and Industry: Lieutenant G. S. Burdick, US Navy, after a test career with the Navy, became Engineering Test Pilot and Manager for the Navy side of the North American Aviation Inc in Columbus, Ohio; Flight Lieutenant Geoff Cairns remained within the Ministry and eventually became the Superintendent of Flying at Boscombe Down; recently he has been putting his expertise into perfecting the flying qualities of the Trago Mills SAH-1 basic trainer. Flight Lieutenant G. W. F. 'Chuck' Charles remained for over twenty years in the UK testing scene and was CO Experimental Flying at Farnborough at the end of the 1970s.

One of the sadder features of 1956 was the final departure from ETPS of Group Captain Sammy Wroath. It is hard to over-emphasise the extent of his input to the School, having been in at the very beginning in 1943, being largely responsible for setting the whole affair on a correct course, and then coming back into the 'Head-master's' chair for another three-and-half years to straighten out its course through the 1950s.

In his place came Group Captain R. E. 'Paddy' Burns, CBE, DFC, a forceful character who originated from Northern Ireland, became a civil engineer then joined the RAF in 1934. He was one of the few officers to gain the DFC in the 1930s, for his efforts with 6 Squadron in the Arab Revolt in Palestine in 1936. His war involved the torpedo side of Coastal Command, rising to command the Torpedo

Development Unit at Gosport and then gaining 254 Squadron with Beaufighters. This Squadron was the torpedo element of the famous North Coates Wing, the first of the big coastal strike Wings which created tremendous havoc amongst German shipping in the North Sea, the Channel and off the Norwegian Coast. The author has vivid memories of Paddy Burns demonstrating, in one of the School's Varsities, just how he would attack a small harbour, choosing Newhaven for his demonstration. Whether the inhabitants of sleepy Newhaven appreciated it as much as we did is open to question.

During the Course Wing Commander Macdonald handed over the Chief Test Flying Instructor's job to Wing Commander E. H. 'Topsy' Turner, AFC, who had been a graduate of No 9 Course in 1950. Three new Flying Tutors arrived to replace Marriott, Johnson and Hubbard; these were Lieutenant Commander R. M. Crosley, DSC, and Squadron Leaders P. P. Baker, AFC, and W. I. O. Morrison, AFC. The Course numbers were now down to twenty-eight comprising four Canadians, three Air Force, one Navy, a Dutch civilian test pilot from Fokker, three Americans (two Navy, one USAF), one Australian, one Frenchman and two Indians. Again the School had a whole Course without a fatality; it seemed that the foundations laid afresh by Sammy Wroath were yielding good results.

One of the weaknesses of the School's present facilities had been the lack of rotary wing aircraft for the growing helicopter empires which were appearing in the Services. To remedy this, a Dragonfly HC 1, VX595, was acquired in April 1957. This was Westland's production version of the Sikorsky S 51 and was no easy aircraft to fly, especially to fixed-wing pilots. It expanded the School's range considerably, although at first it was a difficult machine to absorb into the curriculum. The McKenna Trophy was taken on 16 Course by a Navy man, Lieutenant Commander T. C. Evans,

but there was a cloud on the horizon for those who were going into British test flying.

It was in 1957 that the infamous Defence White Paper was issued by Duncan Sandys which intimated that manned aircraft would no longer be important for aerial warfare and that it would all be done by missiles. This raised a question mark about the future of those leaving ETPS that year and even, perhaps, about the existence of the School itself. Despite that, several of the British students have made successful careers in British Aviation. For example, Flight Lieutenant Mike Goodfellow stayed in the Service testing for a while, becoming a tutor at ETPS from 1966–67 and then moved out to Hawker Siddeley at Hatfield, where he rose to Chief Test Pilot and was responsible for the emergence of the British Aerospace 146, retiring from this post in 1985.

It seemed as if the prognostications about the future of test flying subsequent to Duncan Sandys were coming true with the arrival of No 17 Course in 1958 for there were only twenty-four students. Mr Lang's place as Chief Ground Instructor had been taken over by Mr W. G. S. Port, the last civilian to fulfil this rôle at Farnborough. Squadron Leaders J. M. Crowley and N. F. Harrison, DSO, DFC, arrived as tutors, both old Course members. Otherwise the staff remained as in 1957. Meteor NF 11s, the two-seat night-fighter version, were added to the fleet, as was a Sea Venom FAW 21 but this was of more than ordinary interest because it was a development aircraft fitted with blown flaps, ie, flaps which had engine-driven air blown over the top surfaces when extended which made them more fully effective at slow speeds. Such devices were already planned for the Navy's new Scimitars and, further ahead, for the Blackburn NA 39, which became the Buccaneer. So, for once, the School had one aircraft in the forefront of aerodynamic development. Apart from the

British contingent No 17 Course had three Americans, two Indians, a Canadian, an Australian and an Italian.

One accident took place on the Course, to a Meteor NF 11, and resulted in the death of Lieutenant W. R. Shackleton, RN. Two more had been killed before the 1960s were out, otherwise the Course has survived. Captain H. Andonian, USAF, went on to a career at that mecca of test flying, Edwards Air Force Base, and his two American compatriots, both Navy men, resumed their Navy careers.

By the end of 17 Course the Empire Test Pilots School had been at Farnborough for just over a decade and had passed out eleven courses successfully. It had come on a long way from those hectic days when it moved somewhat peremptorily from Cranfield when the School was still adjusting to peacetime conditions and requirements. It had by now established a firm modus operandi, had acquired an international reputation, so much so that foreign nations like the Americans and French, who had their own test pilots' schools, were happy to send students every year to Farnborough. This built up an exchange whereby British Service test pilot students studied at the foreign schools,

Instructor and student ensconced in Meteor NF 14 *WS845* prior to a sortie. As can be seen, the cockpit layout has been modified, the radar being taken out and test instruments installed.

At the height of the ETPS 'busy' season, and in glorious summer sunshine, the School's flight line looked like this in 1960. Two Vampire T 11s, *WZ451* and *WZ475*; Meteor T 7*WH231'8'* and Meteor NF 14 *WS845'6'* are awaiting their second detail of the morning. The Chipmunk is outside F shed, the ETPS hangar, with the Flight Offices in the background. The little shed in the foreground is the timekeeper's office and next to it, the ground crew's accommodation, entitled 'Refreshments'. In the right background are the water tanks where the Comet fuselage were tested to destruction to discover the fatigue cracks which caused early Comet disasters.

each nation accepting the other's standards.

The 1950s had been a big test for ETPS for it was the period when all the new advances which had been in the pipeline, consequent upon the development of jet propulsion, had burgeoned and the demand for test pilots within the United Kingdom had been great. The School had weathered this demand and not only had met it but had increased its own standards and professionalism in the process. It had benefited greatly by being at Farnborough and the crossfeed with the Establishment, both formal and informal, provided a good environment for young men entering on a test career. The School was to remain at Farnborough for another decade before

external forces drove it away; but this was a more insecure decade for the overwhelming confidence in the future of British military and civil aviation, which had fed all the work of the 1950s, had been dealt blows from Westminster, which made the future both insecure as to the way aeronautical development would be going and also unsure as to whether the political masters had a desire to afford the research and development which such a successful enterprise would require. As the School faced up to its second decade at Farnborough, and entry into the 1960s (a decade in which Britain as a nation lost its way), the future began to look much less rosy than had been the immediate past.

CHAPTER 5
The School in the Sixties

On entering its second decade at Farnborough the School still had the same team at the head, Paddy Burns. 'Topsy' Turner and W. G. A. Port. It had been found necessary, with the large Courses going through and the increased administration in the School as a whole, to have a Flying Wing Adjutant as well as the School's adjutant. In 1958 these duties had been taken on by Mr W. J. Watkinson, who was assistant training instructor to Mr Port, but with 18 Course one of the aircrew on the staff, Flight Lieutenant A. V. Godfrey, became Flying Adjutant, and this procedure became normal, the post being largely involved with flying programmes, students' flying records, etc.

Squadron Leaders Kinder and Bainbridge, and Lieutenant Commander Lang, all previous students, joined as flying tutors. The students now had two trophies to compete for because in 1958 the great American research establishment, Edwards Air Force Base at Muroc in California, had presented a cup to be given to the student who made the greatest progress during the Course (on 17 Course it had been won for the first time by Flight Lieutenant R. A. Whyte of the RAF). This was presented at the McKenna Dinner each year at the end of the Course, the social climax of the whole Course to which notable aviation personalities were invited. Numbers were up again on 18 Course as the students assembled at the beginning of 1959, totalling twenty-seven in all; nine had come from foreign shores, three Americans, one Italian, two Indians, one Swede, an Australian and a Canadian. It was during

this year that the fleet began replacing its Meteor NF 11s with NF 14s and its Hunter F 1s with F 4s, the latter a significant change because of the increased tankage available. A Canberra B 2, *WJ730*, was acquired, a new Devon as well, but most significant of all were the Hunter T 7 prototypes, *XJ615* and *XF113*, and the first production Swift F 7. The two-seat Hunter was to become one of the School's greatest assets for it enabled the flying tutors to fly with the students and demonstrate transonic and supersonic characteristics, rather than just leaving the students to find them out, or not, on their own exercises. Flight Lieutenant J. A. Robinson describes this:

'It was the first time that most of us had ever been supersonic and that first time of rolling over and pushing it down at about 60° to pick it up and actually go supersonic — that was fairly thrilling. It was one of those exercises like spinning the Hunter, which wasn't done in those days as an exercise, although we were shown it; but it has been done at the School for many years now. Trying to get information during that short supersonic burst — you hadn't really got time to appreciate the joys, if you like, of flying. You were furiously trying to write, and at the end of a whole session, when the fuel was getting too low to do any more, you would come back feeling glum because you had started with high hopes of this test card you had written out at great length — and you had filled in about the top two lines, and a few things, and you would be wondering if you would ever be able to get enough information to finish. You were only allowed so many hours for the exercise.'

The Swift was potentially a valuable addition in that it was a transonic fighter on which very different characteristics could be demonstrated, but it was plagued with unserviceability.

The Course proceeded normally until it was almost completed, then the School lost its good safety record again. On 19 October 1959, Squadron Leader N. G. Emslie, one of the RAF students, was flying Varsity WF381 on a normal exercise and crashed fatally four miles north of Tangmere. Then, just over a month a later on 24 November, 'Topsy' Turner took off one evening on a ferry flight in the 'new' Devon, WF984, and crashed into the rising ground just beyond Laffan's Plain. He, too, was killed.

Of the graduates from 18 Course, Flight Lieutenant Gordon Corps continued in the test flying field then joined the Air Registration Board, where he became their Concorde Project Officer and was largely responsible for the certification flying, which enabled this advanced supersonic airliner to enter normal passenger airline service with British Airways (as it now is) so successfully.

The McKenna Trophy was won by Squadron Leader H. R. Radford, who eventually served with the British Aircraft Corporation test team; whilst the second holder of the Edwards Award was Flight Lieutenant Jack Henderson who has remained in the Ministry's test scene for twenty years, being awarded an AFC for his work.

At the beginning of 1960 a new team arrived to head up the School. Captain Ken Hickson, now with two AFCs, a veteran of No 4 Course, took the Commandant's mortar board over from Paddy Burns and his No 2 as Chief Test Flying Instructor became Wing Commander W. J. Laidler, ex-11 Course. The Chief Ground Instructor post was now filled by Squadron Leader J. N. Quick, beginning the line of using Service officers to fill this post; his assistant was Squadron Leader Brian Dickinson. Continuity was provided by the flying tutors who remained unchanged. In addition, Flight Lieutenant Vic Avery joined as deputy to Godfrey, the Flying Adjutant. There was no significant change to the fleet in 1960 and the new Course settled in well, comprising twenty-four students. On this Course it was one of the US Navy students, Lieutenant Commander L. N. Hoover, who carried away the McKenna Trophy and 'Murph' Morrison received the Edwards Award.

No 20 Course brought no new change at the top but three new Tutors, Squadron Leaders E. V. Mellor and E. C. Rigg, AFC, and Lieutenant Commander P. S. Davis, DSC. There was only one new type added to the fleet of aircraft. For some time there had been a woeful lack of 'heavies' in the ETPS aircraft, the task being carried by the Hastings TG501; at the end of 1960 the School had borrowed a Shackleton MR 2 from across the field at Farnborough, using it as preview material for No 19 Course. The Royal Aircraft Establishment loaned this aircraft to the School for 1961, enabling the four-engined element of the fleet to be increased by 100 per cent. At one point it acquired the titling 'Royal Navy' on its side, no doubt as a result of the efforts of the three naval students on the Course.

Twenty-three students entered the Course, the usual three Americans and two Indians, supplemented by an Australian, a Canadian and an Italian once more.

As the 1960s progressed and expanded into the '70s, the pattern of test flying in the United Kingdom, and elsewhere to some extent, was to change and the students passing through ETPS from now on became caught up in this changing pattern. There were to be fewer and fewer new types of aircraft to test, and this was not simply the result of Duncan Sandys' White Paper of 1957. It was more a result of the escalating costs which prevented several prototypes being ordered to compete for one requirement: costs prohibited manufacturers producing their own new prototypes 'on spec'. There was, however, still much development flying to be done but slowly at first, then accelerating in the 1970s and '80s, aircraft becoming much more vehicles for advanced systems, weapons systems, radar systems, intelligence gathering systems, jamming systems, flight systems and more to come. As a result, the test pilot being prepared and trained in the 1960s would inevitably be much more likely to carry out this type of test flying, a type of flying requiring a different mental approach in some ways from the largely aerodynamic test pilot of the heretofore. As yet this was not borne in upon the School however, and the Course continued in 1961 much as it had in 1960. It was during this year that the US Naval Air Test Center at Patuxent River, Maryland, with whom ETPS had the most cordial relations, followed Edwards' example and provided the School with a Shield for the runner-up to the McKenna Trophy.

This new Trophy was collected by Flight Lieutenant J. E. C. Mayes, the McKenna itself being carried off by Flight Lieutenant Clive Rustin, who subsequently served in increasingly responsible posts at Boscombe, Farnborough and Boscombe again. The Edwards award went to Flight Lieutenant P. J. Farris, who was unfortunately killed later in a car accident; it had been a clean sweep by the RAF in 1961.

Captain Hickson moved on at the end of 1961 and his place as Commandant was taken by someone for whom the airfield was very well-known indeed. Group Captain Ray Watts, AFC, had grown up in the Farnborough area and had started his aeronautical career as an RAE apprentice. From there he had gone into the RAF as a pilot and served in India, culminating in the command of a Spitfire squadron in Australia, one of only three RAF squadrons which flew operationally from the Australian mainland. After the war he had a period seconded to Westland for production test flying and he was on the point of leaving the RAF when he was posted to ETPS at Cranfield on No 6 Course. Subsequently he served on test flying duties at Boscombe and Farnborough and it was from the other side of the Farnborough runway that he came to ETPS in 1962.

This previous position in the forefront of current R & D flying at Farnborough gave him certain ideas to develop in his new task. On his arrival he had been told that 'ETPS is the most expensive flying club in the world'. He was surprised to find that the syllabus being used was virtually identical to the one that had served him as a student in 1947, whereas he had already been seeing the changes which were taking place in the world of test flying, particularly as testing was moving much more towards systems testing rather than airframe testing. So, during his reign, he made basic strides in modernising the syllabus, ably assisted by Squadron Leader Eddie Rigg. To assist in this approach to systems assessment the current ETPS Fleet was almost useless, being old aircraft into which the new systems could not be incorporated, so Watts turned to the possibility of using simulators and his contacts with the RAE enabled use to be made of some of their installations — particularly for the evaluation of stability and control characteristics, the symbology of head-up displays and similar work. During the progress of the Course Wing

Commander Laidler handed over to Wing Commander Stan Hubbard, DFC, AFC and Bar, as CTFI. Two new tutors arrived, Squadron Leaders R. T. Robinson AFC, and L. R. Moxam.

One of the most significant changes, which had already been set in motion, was the acquisition of two Vickers Viscounts for the School. They were second-hand 700 Series aircraft which had served with various airlines in the US and had come back to Hurn and been re-worked for the School. The first one arrived in January and the second in May 1962. Not only did these provide new aircraft to fulfil the heavy, four-engined side of training but they were suitable aircraft for future systems training and also provided the School with ideal aircraft for their visits to industry and other establishments. This enabled the Hastings to be pensioned off and the Shackleton to be returned to the RAE.

One innovation that Group Captain Watts brought into the syllabus was to take the staff and students on static line parachuting into the sea; remarkably the Ministry agreed to it. Use was made of the RAE's Beverley and it had to be done on a 'voluntary' basis because of the international bunch of students. He even inveigled the School's hapless chaplain to join in; fortunately, as he was standing shivering beside the Beverley on the appropriate morning, word came through from Lyme Bay that the weather was too rough (obviously the Almighty was looking after His own!) and it was cancelled. When the second attempt came up the said chaplain had ensured that his diary was overfull for weeks ahead! One of the students, John Farley, saw it this way:

'My Dutch courage arose from an overwhelming sense of wellbeing at unexpectedly finding myself alive after a parachute jump into the Solent. The Course used to get en-couraged, in various ways, to leave a perfectly serviceable aeroplane at about a couple of thousand feet above the water. In our case the serviceable aeroplane was a Beverley. The exercise was something to do with teaching observation under stress, and we were to jump in several sticks of six or seven chaps and note this and that on exit, during parachute deployment and in descent. After we were fished out of the water and were sitting on a friendly jetty letting the water run out of our kit and us, I found myself leaning up against a large baulk of timber with fellow student Terry Gill and conscious that Stan Hubbard, the CTFI, had his back to the same post on the other side. Terry started to ask me what I had noticed during this and that. I gave him a wink and I kept saying "Nothing". Eventually he said "Why didn't you see anything?" "Had my eyes shut," I said. "Good Lord," said Terry, "When did you open them?" "When I felt my feet get wet," I said. At this, Stan, who was a parachuting nut and had actually completed a USMC course in combat jumping, came round the corner just in time to realise that he had been had.'

No 21 Course was the course of the Williams, no fewer than four being on it. One was a naval Lieutenant, the other three were RAF and what was more confusing was that they had the initials M.R., N.M. and N.R. respectively! There were also two Robinsons, the tutor and a Flight Lieutenant, of whom more anon. A civilian test pilot came along also, Keith Isherwood from English Electric, and over-seas representation comprised three Americans, two Indians and an Australian.

One of the students, Flight Lieutenant J. A. Robinson, had vivid memories of the Course; and of ETPS generally, for he returned as a tutor in 1967, Chief Instructor in 1976 and eventually left the Service to become Deputy, and finally Chief, Test Pilot with British Aerospace at Woodford. He had come from the V-Force and found the sudden surge into academic subjects the most difficult part. He says:

'At the end — the final exams — I knew I was way behind on aero-dynamics and maths so I worked furiously day and night for some weeks. Squadron Leader Dickinson was the CGI and oversaw the open book exams and when the results came out, for some unknown reason, from being just about bottom of the class I was top. In my final report, when I was looking for a glowing recommendation, he said "Robinson was top of the Course — however, this does not reflect his true ability!!"'

He found the flying very different:

'Suddenly, from accepting rules some mysterious being has laid down on the way you fly, you are being made to question all this because, in the future, you are going to be the person to lay down the rules and limits. It was a big thrill, being treated as an adult pilot. In the Service to change even from co-pilot to captain on the same aeroplane you went away and did a two-month course. Here, to fly a brand-new type you would probably be . . . well, I remember one day someone saying "Ah, Robinson, you are down to fly a Hunter this afternoon. Have you ever flown a Hunter before? No? Have you read the Pilots' Notes? That's OK then." — and that was it.

'I still hold the record for the maximum number of runways used on one take-off. Wally Bainbridge was the tutor in the right-hand seat and Doug England the engineer. I had never been in this great four-engined monster with its tail on the ground before (the Hastings) and I wasn't used to piston engines. As I opened the throttles at the end of the runway the aircraft started a slight swing to the right so I put opposite rudder on — and a touch of brake. But now it was swinging to the left so reverse the process. The swings got bigger and more violent and we left the main runway and entered the short runway. We crossed the arrester runway and things got really out of hand. I made the only sensible remark in the entire proceedings, to Wally Bainbridge. It was "You have control" to which the white faced Wally replied "Thank you very bloody much". By masterly use of the throttles he brought it to a shuddering halt at the far end of the runway with Doug England flattened against the side. We were surrounded by fire engines which had followed us down all the runways.'

It was not always the complicated aero-planes that were hard work. One of the exercises carried out on the Devon was the static margins exercise which involved a series of speed runs and trim settings at two different centres of gravity: the results were then reduced into a formula from which the static margin could be estab-lished. The exercise was flown at 12,000 ft (3,658 m) (no oxygen) and was flown by two students, one flying the aeroplane, the other taking the readings and changing the centre of gravity by humping boxes filled with lead shot forwards and back-wards. There was a case on 21 Course where the students had changed around and the second student was up the back of the Devon swinging the lead around when all went silent — the other student got no response. After some time he trimmed the aircraft and half slid out of the seat from where he could see his compatriot out cold, the exertion and lack of oxygen had taken its toll. The Devon was brought down in height, he came round and the exercise was completed,

Of course asymmetric flying was part of the course and this could be dodgy on the Meteors and Canberras for they both had a large engine fairly well out on the span of the wings. It was this exercise which brought about the one fatal accident on this Course. Flight Lieutenant D. 'Tubby' Oldham, AFM, was on an asymmetric approach in Canberra *WJ730* on 25 October and, as he tried to overshoot, the aircraft slowly turned inverted and crashed upside down on the runway, killing him and Doug England, the flight engineer who was with him. Before the decade was out three of 21 Course had been killed: Flight Lieutenant R. L. Beeson, AFC, on a Hunter at Boscombe Down in 1968; Flight Lieutenant Bill Mackison in one of the RAE's Buccaneer S 1s at West Freugh in 1966; and Captain J. I. Meeker, USAF, who won the McKenna in 1962, in an Air National Guard F-100 in 1965.

One of the three Williams, Flight Lieutenant Neil Williams, joined Weapons Flight at Farnborough and whilst there developed his aerobatic flying, becoming National Aerobatic Champion in 1963 and remaining in this position for five years, acknowledged as one of the finest display pilots ever. His landing of a Zlin with a broken wing spar by descending inverted and half-rolling out a few feet above the runway, remains as one of the classic feats of cool-headed airmanship of all time. By then he had left the RAF and joined Handley Page as test pilot involved with the Jetstream. He was eventually killed ferrying a Spanish-built Heinkel He 111 from Spain to England.

One of the points which had been nagging the Commandant, Ray Watts, was that there was no attempt to run a test pilots' syllabus specifically for the helicopter pilots. He thought it would be the most difficult innovation to introduce into the School but in the event it was one of the easiest. He recalls:

'It started off with writing a paper pointing out that taking a fixed-wing pilot, giving him a fixed-wing test pilots' course for the best part of a year and then giving him twenty hours on a Dragonfly and nominating him as a helicopter test pilot was not the right way to promote the whole concept of flight test for military helicopters. This was accepted fairly easily at the Ministry — provided that the costs were not increased in any way. By good fortune, working out a syllabus for the helicopter pilots and using the costing data from the RAE we were able to prove, much to my surprise, that it would be cheaper so we got authority to carry on. Again, we were very fortunate in having some excellent people that we got in to set up the syllabus and do all the fundamental report writing. Roy Moxam, who went on to become Westland's Chief Test Pilot, was in fact the head man who did most of it for me and Brian Dickinson on the ground side was also extremely valuable.'

So with the onset of 1963 and No 22 Course, along came with it No 1 Rotary Wing Course. To herald this specialisation a Navy Whirlwind HAS 7 was added to the two Dragonflies. An addition to the fixed-wing side was a Supermarine Scimitar, a beautiful-looking, twin-engined, transonic naval fighter which was a maintainer's nightmare. The only addition to the tutors was Lieutenant Commander John Humphreys from the Navy.

For the Rotary Wing Course came Lieutenant Gordon Cryer from the Navy, Flight Lieutenants M. C. Ginn and Rod Mundy from the RAF and Captain J. P. R. Jackson of the Army Air Corps, the first person from this gallant band to come on to an ETPS Course. Three Americans, one Canadian, an Indian and an Italian made up the overseas input and the balance of the twenty-five students came from the RN and RAF.

The Course was carried through successfully — the Rotary Wing side of it being a little disjointed at first because of limitation of equipment and the need to develop the instrumentation on the aircraft as the courses proceeded. But all in all the year was a success and when the McKenna Dinner came around there were now five trophies to be awarded, Westland having added a trophy for the best all-round student on the Rotary Wing Course. Lining up for the trophies at the end of 1963 were Flight Lieutenant Mike Adams for the McKenna, Flight Lieutenant John Farley for the Patuxent Shield, Flight Lieutenant P. Ashoka of the Indian Air Force and Flight Lieutenant Rod Mundy joint winners of the Edwards Award and Flight Lieutenant M. C. Ginn took the Westland Trophy for the first time. Ashoka also qualified for the Hawker Hunter Trophy.

John Farley recalls that he actually applied for ETPS in 1951 when he was an engineering apprentice at Farnborough and his room in the hostel looked out over the ETPS Mess. In 1953 he obtained an interview with Sammy Wroath, the then Commandant, who patiently pointed out that he would have to go away and learn to fly first. This he did and ten years from that interview (which had taken place in 1953) he was on the Course! From ETPS he was posted to Aerodynamics Flight at the RAE at Bedford, at a time when they were flying all the 'weirdies' (HP 115, Fairey FD 2, BAC 221, Short SC 1, Hunting H 126 and Hawker P 1127). John converted to the P 1127 which he found fascinating but frustrating due to the time limitations on the engine. Subsequently he left the RAF and moved to Hawker at Dunsfold for Harrier test-flying, eventually succeeding

Duncan Simpson as Chief Test Pilot. He will be remembered for his frequent demonstrations with a Harrier of a near vertical climb-away from a vertical take-off, by rotating the aircraft about the engine nozzles.

He remembers talking to Jerry Skyrud, one of the two US Navy students, about the Scimitar. He was just about to fly it after Jerry had carried out his first sortie. 'Hey, John', said Skyrud, 'that's quite some airplane. Do you know the climbing speed?' John admitted that he did not. 'Well, you take my tip,' came the reply, 'You hang on to the first one you get'. That remark, says John, said everything about the Scimitar.

Major Bill Pogue, USAF, had a great desire to be an astronaut but felt that his age was not on his side. However, it was not possible for him to qualify without being a test pilot so he went through the Course in 1963 and then served a tour on Weapons Flight at Farnborough. Following this, he was accepted for space training and eventually soared into space with Skylab IV. As John Farley put it, 'his eventual VTO got him roughly 1,000 times higher than mine'.

In 1964 Ray Watts kept much the same team except for a change round in tutors. Squadron Leader Bill Stevens, DSO, AFC, took Roy Moxam's place on the rotary side whilst Squadron Leaders Mike Bruce, AFC, and Murph Morrison moved in as Mellor and Robinson moved out. Twenty-four students arrived with a strong contingent from other services including two Italians, two Canadians and an Australian, as well as the usual one Indian and three Americans. Strides were made in the direction of adapting the syllabus for systems testing and Squadron Leader Eddie Rigg was instrumental in this, using the Viscount techniques, giving the students a systems approach. The Commandant was also aware that, with the cycle of new aircraft in the industry becoming very much extended, flight test teams would be working perhaps two generations of aircraft beyond their last product. He saw the possibility of using the School as an asset to industry in this respect. He therefore set up one-day symposia, inviting members of the industry to join with the School on important topics such as inertia coupling, stable stalling — any point of focus which was relevant to the testing problems of the day. They brought cross-fertilisation between the School and industry where they were enthusiastically supported.

Group Captain Watts had established a good friendship with Chuck Yeager who was his opposite number at Edwards Air Force Base and this presaged an extension of the interchange visits between the American and British Schools. With the Viscounts in the fleet it was now possible to make visits to the USAF and USN Schools at Edwards and Pax River. These provided a considerable interchange of

valuable expertise as well as enabling the British staff to fly some of the American types which otherwise they would not lay their hands on.

The international character of the ETPS is heightened by this system of liaison and exchanges with other countries. Student training exchanges take place with L'Ecole du Personnel Navigant d'Essais et de Reception (EPNER) at Istres in France, and the United States Naval Test Pilot School at Patuxent River, Maryland. ETPS staff visits take place between these two establishments and, in addition, Reparto Sperimentale Volo (the Italian Flight Test Centre at Rome), the United States Aerospace Research Pilot School at Edwards Air Force Base, California, and the Aerospace Engineering and Test Establishment at Ottawa.

For 23/2 Courses in 1964 two valuable additions to the fleet were obtained. One of the development Westland Scout helicopters was added for the rotary wing

A big step forward was made in 1962 with the acquisition of two Vickers Viscount airliners for the School. Not only did they provide valuable training for students in turboprop and multi-engined handling, but enabled airliner testing exercises to be flown. One of the most valuable aids they provided was the ability to lift staff and students and take them in trips worldwide to other test establishments.

The Indians were pretty regular in subscribing to the ETPS courses. Flight Lieutenant K. L. Narayanan, on the left here, was one of the first to specialise on rotary wing aircraft, on No 2 Rotary Wing Course in 1964.

students, bringing a more modern helicopter alongside the three ageing Sikorsky types. The fixed-wing addition was a Twin Pioneer. This STOL machine, used for flying in and out of jungle clearings, was a tremendous asset for its slow-flying capabilities widened the performance envelope for the students and its peculiar characteristics were unlike any other aircraft at the School. Even its atmosphere was different. On entering the cabin one was faced with two rows of wicker chairs, reminiscent of 1920s' airliners and one climbed a steep ascent between them, so exaggerated was the ground angle, eventually reaching the flight deck in the nose. It was a very pleasant aerial carriage and this author remembers flying one mellow autumn afternoon with a low sun and everything outside golden and looking

across from the right-hand seat to observe the tutor, who shall remain nameless, in the left-hand seat asleep and gently snoring!

In addition to the tutors, the School had quite a large staff of non-test pilot aircrew, to operate the Viscounts primarily, with pilots Flight Lieutenants Laurie Adlington and Bill McCausland, navigator Flight Lieutenant Ian Galletti, and engineers Flight Lieutenant Don Pope, Flying Officer Les Lowery and Flight Lieutenant Roy Betteridge, who doubled as Adjutant Flying.

No 23 Course had one fatality during the year and one which was never fully explained. Captaine M. Bigois had been leader of the French national aerobatic team, *Le Patrouille de France*, and was the first Frenchman on the Course for some time. On 24 June 1964, he was returning in the prototype Hunter T 7 from an exercise along the South Coast under radar control (it was a hazy, sunny day) and on the way back, he hit a hill near Hindhead. The only possible explanation was a misread altimeter but no cause was ever fully established. Another aircraft was lost, the Scimitar. Group Captain David Bywater, then a Flight Lieutenant student, tells how:

'One of the exercises for which the Scimitar was used was to investigate lift boundaries, for this aircraft had a very distinctive buffet followed by a pitch up, followed by a wing drop. On 16 July I got the first exercise on it and I hit this particular phenomenon at about 1.3 Mach, pulling through the buffet and the aircraft did something quite extraordinary at about 30,000 ft (9,150 m) and I sort of blacked out at the time. When I came to at about 23,000 ft (7,600 m) the manoeuvre had been completed and that was that. I tried to diagnose what had happened whilst the second student, the RCAF Flight Lieutenant Barry Gartner, took off for the South Coast to complete the same exercise. He had the same sort of problem but in his case, when he came to, the aircraft seemed to be semi-closed down electrically. In fact we later found what had happened was that the "g" reversal from quite a large positive "g" in the pitch up to quite a large negative "g" and then back around 1 "g" in the wing drop had actually thrown the crash switches and he was left with little or no electrics, engines in a stall condition because he had no booster pumps, and so on. Eventually he ejected from the aircraft at low level just off West Wittering but having strapped in incorrectly his leg restraint held him to the seat and he went into five feet of water, four hundred yards offshore. By taking a deep breath and bending down he undid himself from the seat and waded ashore to cheers from the holidaymakers. That was the end of the Scimitar.'

Captain Al Worden, USAF, on the left, takes a compatriot for a flight in the School's Devon in 1964. Later he became the second ETPS graduate into space as Command Module Pilot of Apollo 15.

David Bywater ended the Course sharing the Patuxent Shield with USAF Captain Al Worden, who became the second ETPS graduate into space; he was Command Module Pilot of Apollo 15, circumnavigating the moon in his travels. Bywater has remained in the Service test flying field ever since, having served at Boscombe Down and Farnborough, where he was Wing Commander Flying, and is now Commandant at Boscombe Down as an Air Commodore.

Gliding was still one of the highlights of the ETPS Course and David Bywater relates how on one trip he cast off from his Chipmunk tug under a cumulo-nimbus cloud which promptly enveloped him and took him skywards at 5,000 ft (1,525 m) a minute and popping him out downwind from Farnborough. He laboriously worked his way back but was obviously not going to make the airfield, and Farnborough airfield is surrounded by woods. However, the National Gas Turbine Establishment at Pyestock had playing fields so he tried for these. In the corner was a cricket pitch which was temporarily unused as the same clouds had rained the match off. He aimed to put his craft down between the stumps and actually touched down between them but his approach had given him too high a speed and he ended cutting a groove across the nearby bowling green and eventually stopped in the wire mesh of the tennis courts. An apology to the Director of NGTE ensued!

Another of the students, Tony Hawkes, was later a test pilot at Woodford and he recalls the very first test the students were given. It was the cockpit assessment test, and a challenging test it was whereby the tutors were looking to see if one could arrange one's ideas logically and systematically. The idea was that one had to get into an aeroplane and describe the function and operation of every switch, clock, dial, instrument, lever or anything else in the cockpit, mentioning each position in which these bits could be put. Then one had to assess every one of them as to whether they were good or bad, both in location and operation. Then the view outside the window, or lack of it, had to be assessed and criticised. It really was a demanding exercise and often the hangar at night was full of people in the dead of night, crawling over aeroplanes, saying 'I'll just take another look at this lever', 'Does that switch operate this way or that;' and so on.

The aircraft Tony Hawkes enjoyed most was the Scimitar. 'It was a horrible aeroplane really but it was enormously powerful. Yet it didn't actually go very well despite all the power — it was fun sitting between the enormous air intakes, sucking and breathing and banging and the beat of the engines — it was like being in an express train. It climbed at an enormous rate, 0.9 Mach and that was its level flight speed — it wouldn't go any faster and it wouldn't turn.' The Scimitar, in its brief period at the School, seems to

Another of the problems that most students found testing was the amount of advanced mathematics that they had to absorb and use. Squadron Leader L. R. Moxam, the tutor, is here explaining the intricacies of tethered hovering to Flight Lieutenant K. L. Narayanan of the Indian Air Force and Flight Lieutenant John Strong of the RAF on No 2 Rotary Wing Course.

One of the more testing exercises that rotary-wing students had to perform at ETPS was the tethered hovering exercise, with the tutor reading off pull forces to check the accuracy of the hover. This student is using the Westland Scout, *XR436*, for the exercise at Farnborough in 1964.

have burnt its memory deep into many of the students!

Lieutenant M. Hope was one of the naval helicopter pilots to come on to No 2 Rotary Wing Course. He came from having served on the Wasp Intensive Flying Trials Unit, so his experience was more up-to-date than any of the aircraft which he would fly on the Course. He had the impression that the rotary wing people were worked harder than the fixed-wing men. One of his surprises was the number of fixed-wing aircraft the helicopter pilots flew. To do an air thermometer calibration he was given a Canberra B 2 to fly, never having handled a jet before. The tutor just sat beside him and told him what to do! Also he found that, at that stage, there was no divergent ground school for the rotary wing men, they were still thrown in with the others, which made some of the work difficult for them. For his Preview he was given the Skeeter, an Army chopper borrowed from Middle Wallop.

The Preview is in effect the graduation exercise of the School. The student is given

In September 1964 the School celebrated its 21st Anniversary and laid out a static display of representative types of aircraft used over those years for the benefit of the guests.

an aircraft type he has never flown before (often by courtesy of Farnborough or Boscombe) and is given eight to ten hours' flying on it, during which he has to make a complete written assessment of the performance and handling of the aircraft.

At the end of the Course three of the students were considered not to have reached a sufficiently high standard to graduate — it was a close thing and caused some heartaches afterwards, especially as some of them went on to work in the test establishments at Farnborough.

One of the headaches for the Commandant was always that of the costs of the School being different to the desires of the Treasury. Whilst in the post, Ray Watts had seen the basic unfairness of the way in which the foreign students were being costed. The argument was, that the School and its staff and aircraft and basic overheads were necessary in order to train the test pilots for the British Services — the overseas students need only be costed for the extra flying they did, the food in the Mess and similar incidentals. This was all

very well when there were plenty of British students going through but the time came when, as a result of an overhasty disestablishing of test pilot posts, the numbers required for the British services fell for a number of years so the cost per head went up dramatically because the basic costs were being carried, not by the overseas students, but by the fewer number of British students. Inevitably, rumours were generated that it would be better to close the school and train our men abroad, which would never do for ETPS was the forerunner of all the schools and internationally a leader. There was not much that Watts could do about this situation as Commandant but, in the 1970s, when he became Director of R & D Flying, he gradually, over a period of three years, increased the cost of overseas students to bring it up to a more realistic level with the running of the school.

He was also worried about the School being at Farnborough. In his opinion, it was inadequate for the School's purposes because the airfield is in a hollow with a

OVERSEAS CONTINUATION TRAINING FLIGHTS·EMPIRE TEST PILOTS SCHOOL

With its two Viscounts, the School was able to expand its outside visits to liaison trips beyond UK shores in the sixties. This mid-sixties display map shows their travels.

town at one end and a canal at the other. Because it is a research airfield there are all kinds of installations on the airfield beside the runways. With the School activity the programme had to be worked very closely in with RAE's programme and at rush-hour times the circuit became very over-crowded, especially at lunch times. So he began writing papers which aroused passionate feelings in many but which had their outcome a few years after he had left the Commandant's chair.

1965 was to be Ray Watts' last year as Commandant. Stan Hubbard relinquished the post of CTFI and in his place came Wing Commander Peter Bardon, DFC, AFC, who had previously been a student on 14 Course. Two new tutors arrived to succeed Robbie Robinson and Roy Moxam. These were Squadron Leader Ian Keppie for fixed-wing and Squadron Leader John Hurll for the rotary side. Roy Betteridge, who had come in 1964, was the Flying Wing Adjutant. For No 24 Fixed Wing and No 3 Rotary Wing Courses fifteen students arrived at Farnborough, no fewer than four of them being Indians. The US Army

also sent a candidate in company with the usual two USAF and one US Navy students. An Australian and an Italian made up the overseas contingent. There was no change in the aircraft complement and already students were complaining that there was no real supersonic aircraft in the fleet, for some of the students were used to flying such aircraft in their oper-ational assignments. This was a continual worry to the staff through the 1960s.

The Course was marred by two fatal accidents. On 11 March Squadron Leader O. P. Mathur, a student from the Indian Air Force, was flying Meteor T 7 *WH231* in the circuit and crashed at Minley. Then on 29 June, Squadron Leader John Hurll was flying the CTFI in Dragonfly *WG662*, in the course of which he was converting him to helicopter flying, and the aircraft crashed on the Hog's Back east of Farnham. John Hurll was killed, Peter Bardon was rescued but was badly injured. These accidents, particularly the latter, put something of a damper on the Course and initially impeded the rotary training but thereafter there were no further accidents. The

Australian, Flight Lieutenant Stu Fisher, RAAF, carried off the McKenna Trophy and the Patuxent Shield went to the Italian, Captain L. Fe d'Ostiani. The Edwards Award went to Lieutenant W. Davies of the US Navy and the Westland Trophy to Lieutenant Commander L. G. Locke. The Hawker Hunter Trophy also went to Fisher.

At the end of 1965 Ray Watts left after a longer than usual tour as Commandant, during which he had revamped much of the School's organisation and methods. His place was taken by Group Captain W. J. P. Straker, AFC, who had been a graduate of 9 Course in 1950. He took over a very going concern: Wing Commander Peter Bardon was recovering from his injuries in the Dragonfly accident and was able to take a more active part again. Squadron Leader C. B. Stribling took Dickinson's place as CGI and Lieutenant

Commander Ian Normand and Squadron Leader Mike Goodfellow joined as tutors. Nos 25 F/W and 4 R/W Courses had an even wider spread of overseas participants in 1966. The School was now treating as normal the three Americans, two Indians, one French and one Italian contingent but this time there was a fourth American, two Australians, a Canadian, a South African and two civilians — Mr A. van der Schraaf from Fokker in the Netherlands and Mr D. Wachtel from VFW in Germany. This still left room for plenty of RAF, and RN candidates, plus one from the Army Air Corps. The Course proceeded right through without serious accident although one of the Whirlwinds, *XJ759*, was written off in September.

For a long time one of the School's particular weaknesses had been the lack of a true supersonic aircraft. In fact, many of the Americans on successive courses, who

The School began catering for rotary-wing test pilots in 1958 with two Westland-Sikorsky Dragonfly HC 3 helicopters. Hovering over the School's Flight Offices at Farnborough is *WG662'28'*, the second of the two, and the one in which Squadron Leader John Hurll was killed and Wing Commander Peter Bardon injured, on 29 June 1965.

The accident to the Dragonfly in 1965 highlighted the paucity of the School's helicopter fleet and thereafter, for a long time, its principal type became the Westland Whirlwind. This HAS Mk 7 *XK907*, was one of the most used aircraft in the School's fleet.

were used to flying such aircraft in the normal course of events, were most scathing about the fleet content of ETPS. Despite many appeals the Powers that Were had been adamant that no such aircraft were available for the School. If it was to be, it would have to be a two-seat Lightning T 4, this being the only British type available and these were all urgently required to build up the growing RAF Lightning force. At last, in May 1966, a two-seat Lightning arrived at Farnborough for the School. It was *XL629* which was the second prototype and which had carried out most of the development flying after the loss of the first prototype. So, on paper, the School was now supersonic. In practice, however, there were problems. First of all, this was a non-standard airframe so that spares, from the Lightning production line, would not necessarily fit the aircraft. Secondly, Farnborough had never had any experience with Lightnings up to this point. Consequently, the aircraft spent much of the rest of the year in the hangar giving Tommy Thompson and his maintainers one big headache.

At the end of the Course Group Captain Straker donned the Commandant's mortar board at the McKenna Dinner and supervised the presentation of the prizes — Captain D. T. Ward, USAF, took the McKenna and went on to command the USAF Test Pilots' School at Edwards Air Force Base, and one of the Australians, Flight Lieutenant J. H. Cox, took the Westland Trophy. The Patuxent Shield went to Flight Lieutenant John Lewis, who later served with Aero Flight at Bedford then joined Rolls-Royce, and the Edwards Award to another helicopter student, Lieutenant P. J. G. Harper, RN, whilst the Hawker Hunter Trophy, which was now presented to the best syndicate Preview, went to a trio of RAF Flight Lieutenants, D. W. Gates, S. G. Pearce and N. R. J. Wingate.

The team remained much the same for 1967, with Flight Lieutenant Chuck Taylor taking over from Roly Moss as Adjutant (flying), Fred Miller joining Tommy Thompson in the hangar and Squadron Leaders J. C. K. Baerselman and B. Hopkins joining as tutors. Two dozen students arrived from the customary sources. The Course followed the same pattern as already laid down but throughout the year there was an undercurrent of rumours. For some years now Farnborough had had more than its fair share of alarming rumours — that the whole place would close down; that all the flying would be transferred to Bedford/Boscombe/Pershore, or any one of them; the ETPS would be hived off. The latter became more than an unsubstantiated rumour during 1967 and well before the year was out it hardened into being a fact. Soon the members of 26 Fixed Wing and 5 Rotary Wing Courses knew that they would be the last test pilots to be trained at Farnborough.

The Hunter, in its various forms, has long been a useful tool of the School. This F Mk 6, *XF375*, served for a long time with ETPS at Farnborough and Boscombe Down and is seen in a testing pose in the late sixties.

Already the traffic in and out of Heathrow had become more and more of a problem and, whilst it passed overhead at a respectable height, its passage increasingly restricted the mobility of Farnborough's aircraft. Both ends of the main runway, to say nothing of the cross runways, were becoming increasingly built up and, as already described, the shape of the airfield and its environs made operating more and more difficult for aircraft like the Lightning, which approached at 175 knots and required a reasonably clear approach path. Ray Watts had already gone into print about all this a year or two before and at last notice was being taken.

So it was at the end of the year that the last McKenna Dinner was held in the famous ETPS Mess and it was a particularly international bunch of winners who gathered the trophies. The McKenna went to Lieutenant Commander V. W. Klein of the US Navy; the Westland Trophy went to Flight Lieutenant V. L. P. Galvin, RCAF; the Patuxent Shield to Squadron Leader B. J. Graf of the Royal Australian Air Force and the Edwards Award to Flight Lieutenant A. D. A. Cooke of the RAF. The syndicate which took over the Hunter Trophy comprised Lieutenant Commander Klein, Lieutenant Commander R. C. O'Day of the Royal Australian Navy and Flight Lieutenant George McIntosh, RAF. Just as all this was happening Robbie Robinson was rejoining the School as a tutor. He recollects:

> 'It was very sad because we were losing that marvellous ETPS Mess, which had been the centre for test pilots in the UK for many years. I had just arrived in time for the last students from the 1967 Course just leaving — there were a few still around; one, an Australian, I think he was, with a broken leg who had to be held back. I understand he broke it falling off the top of the bar! The

The great social occasion of the ETPS year was the McKenna Dinner, held as the culmination of the year's Course, when all the results, and the Trophy winners, were known. At this dinner the Commandant traditionally donned the 'headmaster's mortar board' hat as his badge of office to present the trophies. In this instance, it is Group Captain W. J. P. Straker, AFC, in 1967.

last farewell party went on for about three weeks — every night was a farewell party. We were trying to drink up the profits of the Mess and consequently making more and more profits because industry used to support the Mess in those days.

'The ETPS Mess had certainly been the hub of Farnborough for the whole of the time that it was there. It was totally self-supporting — it had its own PMC, its own Mess Secretary, and indeed it was pretty well equipped and had obviously been going since the days just after the war. I think there weren't the manpower shortages that we have now. They had a very dedicated and devoted

staff; it had a jolly good little bar which was certainly the hub of the Farnborough Air Display. Some tremendous parties, and some of the decorations that were produced for the summer and winter balls were almost unbelievable. We had good liaison with the Shepperton Film Studios and used to borrow film sets to make these quite enormously attractive affairs. There was another Mess at Farnborough, No 1 Mess — actually everybody thought it was the first Mess in the Royal Air Force but in fact it was the third. I think Netheravon was the first and then Upavon and finally Farnborough, but it was always called No 1 Mess to distinguish it from the ETPS Mess. Sadly, quite a lot of the silver went missing one year because in those days you had open door during the Farnborough Show, and a lot of people just wandered in and lifted things like cigarette trays and salvers which, by today's standards were not very valuable then but, of course, would be worth quite a lot of money now.'

So ended ETPS's most important era to date. The School had come from Cranfield in 1947, still a somewhat insecure organisation, feeling its way into its important task of preparing pilots sufficiently for the tremendous strides forward in aviation in the 1950s and '60s. At Cranfield it had felt out on a limb; it was divorced from real flying, certainly from the testing scene, and was surrounded with an academic, almost scholastic, environment which had some advantages but was somewhat esoteric for the more high-spirited students of the late 1940s. Coming to Farnborough it found its feet. It was cheek by jowl with those who were practising the task for which the School was training its candidates, the maintainers were used to a diversity of types in the fleet, were no strangers to some of the specialised test equipment which had to be installed, and the RAE itself welcomed and helped the School in a countless number of ways. Through the 1950s and '60s the School had developed and grown in stature, had established firm links with the Industry and with similar schools in France and the United States, had grown in professionalism and flexibility to meet the changing needs of the test environment. Socially, the ETPS Mess had risen high on the lists of Service establishments which were a must for the growing number of military and industry aviation socialites, its welcoming atmosphere and charm having become a byword.

Farnborough, then, had been the making of the Empire Test Pilots' School. The child that had been conceived, born and nurtured at Boscombe Down some twenty-five years before was now returning home a mature adult, ready to hold its own in that mecca of testing professionalism, the Aeroplane and Armament Experimental Establishment at Boscombe Down. Farnborough has ever been the poorer for the School's going. No longer was the circuit to be busy with one aircraft on finals and two or three downwind for most of the day. No longer was there a choice between the staid No 1 RAF Officers' Mess by the Farnborough Road and the racy ETPS Mess near the Queen's. The latter soon became a YMCA Hostel for the RAE apprentices and singles who had nowhere else to live, gone was its élan forever.

CHAPTER 6
Back to Boscombe

The move back to Boscombe was, as has already been said, very controversial and initially the School, from Group Captain Bill Straker down, were not happy with the arrangements that were in hand for them. Air Vice Marshal H. A. Merriman, AFC, was at that time CO of 'A' Squadron at Boscombe Down and also PMC of the Officers' Mess and so was heavily involved in absorbing ETPS at Boscombe. He said that it was very obvious that the School was extremely comfortable at Farnborough and reluctant to move. However, there was also the obvious problem of the costs of running the School, and all the buildings and ancillary facilities were under scrutiny as to whether they could be afforded at a time of major defence economies. The solution seemed to be to move to Boscombe Down which would answer the airfield and airspace problems, mentioned in the previous chapter. It was thought that the different aircraft in the School fleet could be operated by the appropriate test squadrons at Boscombe, ie, the helicopters would go to 'D' Squadron whilst 'A' Squadron would take the Lightning and so on; thereby the engineering cost of maintaining and servicing the aircraft would be hidden away in the overheads of running the trials squadrons. Equally, it was argued that the School should share the normal Officers' Mess both on the basis that again there would be no readily identifiable overhead in maintaining a separate Mess and that there would be the opportunity for the students during the course of the year to rub shoulders with the test pilots who were actively engaged in flying trials on a day-to-day basis. The School did not see eye-to-eye on this approach; they saw the School being totally submerged and losing a great deal of its individual identity, purpose and nature. It would now become a small fish in a big pool, instead of being a major independent flying element as it was at Farnborough.

The move did work eventually, although perhaps not as well as had been hoped. The integration of the School with the Mess meant the feared loss of individuality and did not provide the blend with A&AEE pilots, for the simple reason that the students were too busy in the evenings to mingle. However, the flying rate improved because there were larger engineering resources to look after the fleet; it was now that the DB Lightning two-seater came into its own. But many of the aircraft became joint-user aircraft with the A&AEE fleet, and problems arose when the Establishment wanted to use, for example, one of the Hunters as a chase plane when it was urgently needed by the students. Obviously, A&AEE could usually muster the bigger clout. Inevitably, those who had known the joys of Farnborough were full of woe after the move but it did not take too long before the School began to forget the past and adapt to the present and realise to the full the many advantages that came with Boscombe Down.

The new Course started off slightly disorganised because not all the aircraft had arrived until April 1968. One had even been left behind; this was the Short SB 5. This aircraft had originally been built as a slow-speed experimental machine to explore handling qualities of swept-wing aircraft, its wings being adjustable, on the ground, as far back as 69°, and its tail could be mounted either on the fuselage or at the top of the fin. This had first been used in intensive testing for the Lightning development, then had gone to the RAE at Bedford where Aero Flight used it as one of its aerodynamic freaks for a variety of experiments. When it had had all the possibilities wrung out of it there, it was given to ETPS at Farnborough as early as October 1965 where it was intended as a unique type for the students to sample towards the end of their course. In practice, however, it was such an impossible aircraft to keep serviceable that it hardly ever ventured out of the hangar so, when the School moved, by common consent it was just 'forgotten'.

Basically, the same team moved down for the 1968 Course but soon after the move the CTFI, Peter Bardon, was posted and Wing Commander Reggie Spiers, ex-14 Couse, took his place. Squadron Leader Brian Hopkins, from 20 Course, moved down from his post as OC SME Flight at Farnborough as a tutor, joining Squadron Leader J. A. 'Robbie' Robinson who had already joined the end of the previous course at Farnborough. The ground instruction was still catered for by Squadron Leader C. D. Stribling, BSc, DCAe, CEng, AFRAES, ably assisted by Flight Lieutenant W. A. Turner, BSc, DCAe. The School had a Qualified Flying Instructor (QFI), Flight Lieutenant Bob Sattelle, and his task was to convert the students to the new types, releasing the tutors for the specific testing exercises. For the larger aircraft, there were two navigators, Squadron Leader S. T. McKay and Flight Lieutenant G. F. Stowe and three flight engineers, Flying Officer J. R. Goatham and Flight

The facilities for the ground work in the late sixties compared very favourably with those in the original Boscombe huts. Squadron Leader Stribling is apparently describing some abtruse aerodynamic point to No 27 Course in 1968.

Rotary Wing students Lieutenant Mike Purse, RN, and Flying Officer Brian Skillicorn, RAF, on No 6 Rotary Wing Course, pose for the photographer as they study helicopter aerodynamics.

Lieutenants F. Watson and R. L. Wheeler. In addition, there were two civilian Technical Co-ordination Officers, Messrs I. Butler and B. Day.

The Courses Nos 27 Fixed and 6 Rotary Wing, comprised eight RAF officers, three RN, one Frenchman, one from the US Navy, a Canadian, two Australians, another Army Air Corps officer and an American civilian, Mr Thigpen, from the Flight Department of General Dynamics. The Frenchman, Captaine J. Depui, was killed on 1 October in Canberra *WH715*, otherwise there were no casualties.

At the end of the Course Bill Straker vacated the Commandant's chair for a Station Commander's post in Singapore. His place was taken by a Navy man, Captain Pat Chilton who had gone through

the School in 1948 on 7 Course, when it was in its early days at Farnborough. He and Reggie Spiers, impressed by the much increased professionalism that the School had acquired since last they were there, continued to build upon these foundations for the next two courses.

After moving to Boscombe Down the School had acquired two Beagle Bassets. One had been the RAF pre-production machine and was non-standard, the second was the first full production machine. The Basset was a good example of a reasonable aircraft which had been so altered by RAF requirements as to render it a failure. It had been ordered as a communications machine to replace the Anson (and to support British industry) but the Ministry insisted that it should be modified so as to be able to carry a full V-Bomber crew with all their kit. The drill in those days was that the V-Force, if war approached, would be dispersed all over the country on different airfields and the Bassets would be running shuttle services between bases. Of course, this requirement was really more than the aircraft could handle, so when the aircraft went into RAF service it was not liked. It was a useful aircraft for the School, though, and also provided a comms aircraft to take over from the Devons. During 1969 one of the tutors, Squadron Leader Brian Hopkins, was taxed with the task of developing the possibility of one of these being modified as a variable stability aircraft and in due course *XS743*, the second one, went off to Cranfield where the Cranfield Institute of Technology took it into its workshops and made the necessary modifications.

Seventeen students appeared for Nos 28 and 7 Courses in 1969, a few more from overseas, compared with the previous year. These comprised a French Navy Lieutenant, an Italian Air Force Major, a US Navy Commander, two Australians, a German civilian, a Lieutenant from the Royal Australian Navy, and an Israeli Major. To these were added seven RAF and one RN candidate.

Robbie Robinson, who was now in his second year as tutor, describes the task:

'Once I got my first syndicate I started to thoroughly enjoy it. At the start I was worried that the foreign students would take the badinage of the British students rather poorly and that we would get incidents but, in fact, there was nothing like that at all. It was marvellous give and take, and the Australians used to suffer more, I think, from funny wisecracks than anybody else but they gave as good as they got, if not better. The Italian student (Fabio Colussi) was a super chap, very Roman, very correct, and he was determined that his English

was going to be absolutely perfect by the time he went home — it was jolly good, better than my Italian, and he used to use me as his English tutor as well as his flying tutor. I remember once, ground school was over about nine o'clock in the morning and he came in and said "Robbie, please explain to me when you say 'good evening' and when you say 'good night'?" That's quite a difficult one, especially at nine o'clock in the morning, I thought, and brilliantly I said "Ah, that's easy — you say 'good evening' when you are greeting someone and you say 'good night' when you are saying 'goodbye'." He replied, "Now I understand, thank you, good night!" '

Whereas in the early days of ETPS most of the students coming through the pipeline had either test flying experience already or at least a broad spectrum of types flown, often operationally, now, in the 1970s, the variation in background experience was quite marked. Wing Commander Martin Mayer, then a Flight Lieutenant, sheds quite some light on being a rotary wing student on No 7 Rotary Wing Course:

'It was about early 1968 when I had a phone call from a chap in MoD who said that they had no applications from the Royal Air Force for Rotary ETPS and they were phoning everybody who had "A" Level Maths. Was I interested in going? I was still very inexperienced and had no idea what ETPS was. He explained over the phone and said did I think I would like to try — which is very probably the worst way of going on the Course that I can think of. I was accepted for No 7 Rotary Wing Course and I arrived with only two types in my log book (Jet Provost and Whirlwind 10). In addition, my main handicap was not having flown an aircraft with an automatic flight control system, as all modern helicopters have autopilots of one sort or another. I had also not flown anything with more than one engine so I had quickly to learn about twin-engined operation.'

Despite all these setbacks he went on to enjoy the Course and to take away the Westland Trophy. He continues:

'The rotary course at this stage had only two types — the Scout and the Whirlwind 10, borrowed from the SAR people. The two Scouts were, in fact, prototypes, Saunders Roe P 531s, which were rather old and differed quite markedly on some of their major structure from later production aircraft. As it was difficult for them to be modified up to the standard required by the Army they had been handed over to ETPS [the old familiar way in which ETPS, only too often, over the years, had gathered in what others considered rubbish — Author]. They did have their little foibles and the matching of airframe to engine was quite difficult. Also, at that time there were many engine problems with the Nimbus.

'I was used to flying single-engined helicopters so some of the exercises didn't worry me too much — it is only now, when I think back, to things like tethered hovering where we were required to sit in the high hover with the aircraft, that I realise that if the engine had stopped or had a malfunction it would have been catastrophic. It was surprising that the tutors managed to teach us as much as they did. We used to do some fairly frightening things in forward flight as well; to start with, we were amazed at the positions in which the tutors would put the aircraft. They would demonstrate jack stall on the Scout, jack stall, vertical bounce and blade stall, with great aplomb and very relaxed about it — talked to you as you did it, and you hammered around these corners. One realised just how close you were to the thresholds of what the aircraft would do.

'One of the unusual exercises we did to explore the flight envelope, was to take the Scout to its ceiling. Normally, helicopters are limited to 10,000 ft (3,050 m) in service because of the lack of oxygen but on the Course you do a height climb, with oxygen fitted, to 16,000 ft (4,880 m). The height climb involved making the poor little Scout, which was not overly powerful, climb this high where the band of flight envelope available was very, very small. If you went faster than about 65 knots you got into blade stall and if you went slower than 40 knots you got into tail rotor handling problems, so you flew with the collective under your armpit feeling like a pimple on a mountain. Having got there and feeling most uncomfortable, the tutor would lean across and switch off the hydraulic system and you had to do it in manual; at the time I thought they were absolutely mad. Having done it once or twice myself (it is now done on the Gazelle and they go up to 20,000 ft (6,100 m)) it is still a pretty horrific manoeuvre, and just the sort of thing that ETPS seem to delight in.

'As for the other flying which we did on the Course — I took the opportunity, whenever it was offered, to fly in the fixed-wing aircraft and managed Hunter, Lightning, Chipmunk, Basset, Viscount, Argosy and in fact on one of the School's industry visits, I drove an SRN Hovercraft around Southampton Water in the fog. The School had three gliders at the time as well, which one was encouraged to fly: three hours were required of each student. It was not taken too seriously and largely became a weekend hobby: you could have a pleasant sunny day out on the airfield with your family and explore an area of flying which very few of us had previously encountered. We were encouraged to get our "C" rating on the gliders which meant that you had to be airborne for an hour from launch.

'One day, I took off expecting to be airborne for ten minutes if I was lucky. However, I got into a thermal, which I had never been in before, and finished up at three and a half thousand feet going very well but being blown towards Bournemouth. I decided to try for my "C" but did not have my watch on me so I stuck to my thermal, seeing Boscombe disappearing to the north. I had been told that I had to stay in a certain size of cone over the airfield and I was already outside it, so I realised that if I didn't head back for Boscombe soon I wouldn't make it. I found a little card on the inside of the glider which gave glide angles in different wind conditions, implying that if I got up to sixty knots that would be the best gliding angle for getting home. This I determined to do and pushed towards Boscombe at sixty knots. As I was getting lower and lower I realised that I was not making enough headway and that I was going to drop into a field, probably about two fields short of the airfield, which would have been very undignified. When I arrived over this field I saw that I had still got sixty knots on, so I traded speed for distance and creamed along about six feet above the ground, hopping over the hedges, and eventually fell onto the airfield,

Unusual positions are all part and parcel of the Course flying. The School's Chipmunk will not fly upside down for long.

just. I had been airborne for an hour and five minutes so I got my "C" but I also got a flea in my ear from Pete Normand, the tutor in charge that day, for they had totally given me up and were preparing to come and retrieve me.'

At the end of the Course the students went their ways. Herr K. Koglin, the German civilian, went to the Bundeswehr test squadron, Erprobungstelle 61, at Manching where he was still in action in the eighties. The French, Italian and Australian graduates all went to their respective test establishments. Lieutenant W. S. Loew of the Royal Australian Navy eventually went on to Hawker de Havilland Australia at Bankstown. The RAE claimed Flight Lieutenant Tom Gilmore at Farnborough and Squadron Leader M. Laughlin and Flight Lieutenant Ron Ledwidge at Bedford. Flight Lieutenant Ian Strachan went to Farnborough later as Wing Com-

mander Flying. Lieutenant J. White went on to serve at Boscombe Down and Flight Lieutenant J. D. Blake returned to Boscombe, serving on 'B' Squadron, and later as an ETPS tutor.

For 1970 Captain Chilton and Wing Commander Spiers headed up the team and retained the same fleet of aircraft, except for the loss of two, one of the Canberra B 2s and the original Chipmunk, *WB549*, the first production aircraft which had twenty years of flying behind it. Thus, by reducing the fleet, small economies could be seen to be made. The numbers were down for the 1970 Course (No 29 FW and 8 RW), fifteen students taking part. These included Captain W. Spychiger of the Swiss Air Force, adding another nation to the School's score. The RAAF sent three men on this course; the Americans only one, a Navy man. Comte B. Le Cornec came from the French Air Force and there were two civilian test pilots, A. R. Baker from Canada and H. F. Rammensee from

At the end of 1968 the School bade a sorrowing farewell to Farnborough and its own distinctive Mess, returning to its birthplace, Boscombe Down. At the beginning of 1969 it was all shipshape for that year's course, the School fleet comprising on the fixed-wing side Viscount 745 *XR902*; Canberra B 2; Lightning T 4 *XL629*; Hunter F 6; Basset CC 1; Chipmunk T 10 *WD321*; Scout AH 1 *XR436*.

Germany. Four RAF, and one AAC, men made up the balance. By now the School was getting more into its stride after the move to Boscombe. Reggie Spiers commented:

> 'The assistance we got from Boscombe, which had started fairly lukewarm, had become very good indeed. We got a tremendous amount of support from the Establishment in lending aeroplanes for Preview exercises and so on.'

Of course, by now, the School's reputation was well known throughout the aviation world and it was in the strange position of growing in prestige in this field and yet being continually under the shadow of the axe as successive British governments sought ways of cutting down defence expenditure. It was in 1970, however, that the School received an accolade when its guest speaker at the McKenna Dinner, the culminating focal point of each Course, was HRH the Duke of Edinburgh, himself an accomplished pilot. The CTFI remembers that when all the staff were introduced to him prior to the dinner he asked each one if they were graduates of the School and when this was confirmed he pronounced it quite clearly a 'closed shop'.

At the end of the Course Mr Baker took his newly-acquired skills to the Civil Aviation Department of the Canadian Department of Transport, the Australians went to the Laverton test base. The US Navy's Lieutenant Commander R. K. Pottratz went to NATC at Patuxent River and Herr Rammensee to Erprobungstelle 61 at Manching, as had his predecessor. The Swiss Captain became part of Eidg Flugzeugwerke at Emmen. Four of the graduates remained at Boscombe with the A&AEE, Flight Lieutenants W. G. Gevaux, M. A. Hindley, D. F. Moffatt and M. H. B. Snelling. Mike Snelling later became part of the Harrier team at Dunsfold as Deputy

and then Chief, Test Pilot. Two went to Farnborough, Flight Lieutenants R. G. Davis and B. Peaty. Graham Davis later served at Bedford; Brian Peaty, whilst at Farnborough, was responsible for the most dangerous aircraft on the airfield, a Scimitar with its wings cropped so that it could not fly, which was used for braking tests. It eventually propelled him off the end of Runway 29 at high speed in a determined bid to get to the NGTE at Fleet and that was the end of those trials — but not of Brian Peaty.

In 1971 Captain Pat Chilton left and his place was taken by Group Captain D. P. Hall, AFC. He had been through the Course in 1959. He still had Wing Commander R. J. Spiers as CTFI and some revision of the Fleet took place during this year. The Rotarians had been relying on the two DB Scouts, a loaned Whirlwind 10 and the old Whirlwind HAS 7 which had been brought from Farnborough. This was scrapped in March and replaced by another Mk 10; in addition, one of the Scouts was pensioned off during the year because, in May, an ex-RN Wessex HAS 1 had arrived: still a single-engined helicopter, yet its controls and instruments were a generation forward of the Whirlwind. For the fixed-wing boys another Hunter two-seater was added but, on the heavy side, came the Argosy C 1, a four-turboprop, twin-boomed, tactical transport which became a very useful tool.

Course numbers were up to seventeen; after a pause the Italians and Indians were back together with a Swedish Navy Lieutenant Commander N. C. Hägg. France, Australia, the US Navy and another German civilian made up the foreign contingent, joining nine RAF, and one RN, pilots. Getting the students to arrive at the right moment was not always easy. For example, Flight Lieutenant P. A. Sedgwick had been serving on 48 Squadron in Singapore, flying Hercules, and was posted back to Thorney Island in the autumn of 1970 but at the same time his application for ETPS had come through. Rather than move his family down to the South Coast for a couple of months and then up to Salisbury Plain, it was agreed for him to go to the school in September and work as a general dogsbody in preparation for the next Course. Much of this time was taken up with the Station's preparations for the Royal Visit of 1971. The Queen was scheduled to visit the Station on 19 March and both A&AEE and ETPS pilots put in much hard work lining up a fine flying display. The day, when it came, was one of disappointments; Her Majesty had influenza and could not come but at the last minute Princess Anne gallantly filled in. But the main problem was the weather. The cloud base over the rolling hills around Amesbury was only 600 ft (183 m), with intermittent drizzling rain blowing across the windswept Down and making everyone cold and wet. Reggie Spiers remembers his part in this epic day:

'The weather was absolutely appalling, a howling gale — the cloud was about 600 ft, and to everybody's astonishment, the very courageous Commandant at that time, Air Commodore Roger Topp, decided that we would have the full flying show - which staggered everybody because at one point there would be fourteen different types of aeroplanes, all going in different directions, in the circuit at the same time. ETPS took its part in this display. I was leading the four "slowies" in the Twin Pioneer, with a Harvard on the port wing, a Chipmunk on the starboard and the Basset in the slot. The margin of speed I had to play with was only five knots — if I went any faster than, I think 95, the Chipmunk couldn't catch up, and if I went any slower than 90 the Basset stalled out so it was quite a tricky little operation.

After flying past the Princess in her saluting base we were meant to hover in the local area until the time came to land. In fact, as I turned across wind I could see the "heavies" coming along (Valetta, Varsity, Hercules and Hastings) all at about our height and I could see they were going to pound us into the deck. I couldn't get any lower without writing Dave Scouller off who was in the Basset in the slot at the back, so he peeled off and disappeared in the Reading direction while I landed the rest on the grass at Old Sarum and didn't return until early evening, much to the relief of Roger Topp.'

Another of the aspects of the Course which could produce difficulties was in relation to the families, particularly the foreign students. Peter Sedgwick mentions that, although it was the policy of the School to move their families in two or three weeks early, some of them were only released from their previous units a few days before — some of the foreigners were very late in arriving. 'At that time it was extremely difficult, in fact well nigh impossible, for a student on the Course to be given a married quarter and so everybody was out in "hirings". We were spread out around the countryside in the villages. This didn't matter all that much for the British students but it had a great effect on some of the foreigners — for instance, the Indian family were out in a remote village without much public transport, and I believe that the wife had never been away from home before, certainly never out of India.'

Another of the disadvantages at Boscombe was one of geography on the airfield. The fixed-wing people were, and still are, on the north side of main apron in buildings attached to one of the original hangars, from where they walk out to their aircraft on the hardstanding. The rotary-

Supersonic testing training with the School was solely in the hands of the second prototype Lightning T Mk 4, *XL629*. It had a poor serviceability record at Farnborough but, once it moved to Boscombe, where they had had plenty of experience of Lightnings, things looked up. *XL629* is seen here landing on Boscombe's main runway after clocking up 1,000 mph.

wing people are way across the airfield, the other side of the main runway in the large new hangar forming Boscombe's helicopter emporium. Consequently, in describing his days at ETPS, Peter Sedgwick said:

'There was quite a gulf between the rotary-wing and fixed-wing sides. We didn't really have as many points of contact at all as we would have liked.'

He thought, too, that in his time there was a little bit too much of a chasm between staff and students which led to some of the students trying to beat the system — a crafty student could play off one staff member against another and avoid doing the amount of written work required. On a course such as this, though, to establish this relationship in such a way as to obtain the optimum is a very difficult exercise indeed.

The Course itself was so intensive that there was little time for the social side.

There were a few private parties organised by the students themselves and the tutors would entertain their syndicates and there was the occasional official function. But most evenings saw the students at their books and reports.

By now the School was very much in the way of flying supersonically. Not only was the Lightning regularly flying up to 1,000 mph (1,600 km/h) but the Hunters were flying transonic dive exercises, all of which added up to a regular number of sonic booms, because of which these exercises were flown only over the Channel so that the recipients were ships transiting the Channel, or the seagulls. Peter Sedgwick remembers flying one such exercise over the Channel and as he was recovering from the sonic dive the clouds below parted to show many acres of glinting tomato houses on the island of Jersey! There were no repercussions. But one could also come up against difficulties in the light aircraft:

'Another occasion, I was on a spinning exercise in the Chipmunk and I remember being very engrossed, doing fourteen or more spins — not very far away, near the village of Wylie, just the other side of Salisbury. I remember thinking "I could squeeze in just one more spin", without being properly aware of two rather vital facts — I had done most of my spins in one direction and, therefore, most of my remaining fuel had ended up in one wing, with very little in the other, and the fact that there was a forty knot wind blowing, which made rather a significant difference to a Chipmunk's ability to get even from the other side of Salisbury back to Boscombe Down. I thought of stopping at Old Sarum as I went past and then I thought: "No. A little bit farther and I would be on high finals for Boscombe anyway." I called a bit of priority and landed, taxied up the hill and got out. Shortly afterwards I received a call from the ground crew to the effect that they had put 18½ gallons of fuel in the Chipmunk — I think it holds eighteen!'

One of the means of producing more

One of the unique exercises flown by ETPS is the spinning of swept-wing fighter type aircraft. This is flown on Hunter T Mk 7s and provides the students with real-life experience which they acquire nowhere else. One such trial is graphically shown here by this condensation trail.

economies in the School was now becoming a most important part of the School's fleet. To give a wide spectrum of aircraft types on the School was a necessary but expensive side of the School's operation; to cut this down, one would ideally require one aircraft with variable handling qualities so that all types of control characteristics could be demonstrated on one machine. Already this had been done in America — Cornell University had modifed a B-26 over a decade before. Now the plans laid in the late 1960s had come to fruition, one of the School's Bassets having been modified to a variable stability aircraft.

The aircraft had been modified in such a way that the left-hand pilot, normally the captain, had his control column and rudder pedals connected to the control surfaces in the normal manner so when the pilot in that seat flew the aircraft it flew as any other Basset. On the right-hand side the controls simply operated electrical terminals transmitting signals to a computer which drove the actual control surfaces. In the electrical loop was a potentiometer including a rheostat for varying the stability parameters for each control surface. This potentiometer bank was also fed by inputs from other parameters such as control surface position, yaw, roll, angle of attack, etc, so in the end the aircraft responded between all these different inputs to give a variable stability which could be governed by the demonstrating pilot feeding in appropriate signals on the computer. Much can be demonstrated in this one aircraft; for example the C of G range can be altered and the pilot shown what can happen to control when the CG goes too far aft, Dutch Roll can be simulated in a straight-winged aircraft, etc. To fly a Basset with, say, Vulcan control responses can be a fascinating and instructive exercise.

When the Basset, *XS743*, was used by the School it was simply as a test flying instructional aid; it could not be flown by students solo but necessitated a tutor flying in the left-hand seat with the normal controls and also the controls of the potentiometers so that he had mastery of the whole situation. The student in the right-hand seat could then operate controls in whatever mode was required. Variable Stability flying is never done in the Basset below 3,000 ft (910 m) to give the tutor room to take over and correct if a potentially disastrous situation has arisen from the manoeuvre. For example, one of the most interesting demonstrations is that of Dutch Roll, a motion that an aircraft can automatically take up with divergent rolling and yawing movement; it is a condition which can take place in high-speed swept-wing aircraft in certain conditions. The VSS Basset has been an excellent demonstrator of this condition and has been a very valuable tool in ETPS's range for enabling students to see and understand different, and sometimes dangerous, characteristics.

At the end of the Course it was Peter Sedgwick who took the McKenna and went on to serve at Farnborough, before returning to ETPS as a tutor. After leaving the Service, and after a brief period as an airline pilot, he joined British Aerospace at Hatfield, where he is now Chief Test Pilot and responsible for the ongoing development of the BAe 146 series. Flight Lieutenant John Sadler also went with him to Farnborough, then returned to normal Service flying but is now in the same sphere as Sedgwick, serving in the test rôle at British Aerospace's Chester plant.

Another seventeen turned up for Nos 31 and 10 Courses in 1972. The American input had tailed off very much, no USAF officers appearing now, just one US Navy man each year. The Australians were very keen, sending three RAAF Flight Lieutenants all of whom went back to swell the test pilot force at Laverton. Captain R. A. Dean came from the South African Air Force, another Israeli pilot came as did yet another German civilian. Eight RAF, and one RN, pilots made up the balance. The only fleet addition was a significant one for the Rotary Wing students. At last a large, modern, twin-engined helicopter was available, a Sea King HAS 1, and this

Hunter T Mk 7 *XL579* taxies in after one such spinning exercise in 1969.

The McKenna Dinner traditions were continued at Boscombe Down using the A&AEE Mess. In 1970 the guest of honour was HRH the Duke of Edinburgh, himself a pilot of no mean ability. He can just be distinguished along the top table of this august gathering.

One of the School's pet guests each year for the McKenna Dinner was the celebrated aircraft cartoonist, 'Chris' Wren. Each year he produced a unique cartoon of the personalities of the year's course; these are treasured by the school. The 1971 cartoon is reproduced here.

really enabled the RW tutors to increase the value of the training for their students. Sadly, during May, the two Viscounts which had carried the School on so many visits far and wide, and contributed an airliner input to the School's training, were sold. From now on the School had only its 'Whistling Wheelbarrow', the Argosy, for its travels.

At this time the School had a Commandant, Group Captain Hall, who took a great interest in the rotary-wing side of things. Lieutenant Commander Hope relates that he used to fly with him at least once a week and they usually ended by doing engine-off landings in the Scout, an exercise at which the Commandant became very proficient:

> 'In return, quite frequently, he used to give me a shout when there was a trip going in one of the fixed-wing aircraft. I always remember one of the first times we did this. He called me across to fly the Basset up to Farnborough, telling me to get across early because he hadn't flown the Basset for some time and I hadn't flown it before and we were supposed to be flying some of the fixed-wing tutors to Farnborough. We duly rushed out to the aircraft on the apron and got in — I read out the Pilots' Notes while he did the checks

and one of the first was "Battery Master ON" — there was a long pause while we both searched frantically. He was heard to remark "Have you found it yet?" to which I replied "No" and he said "Neither have I but we'd better be quick as here come the tutors". We eventually found it and that was the way the flight was conducted. We duly got to Farnborough and I was carefully briefed on the landing but unfortunately my only landing in the Basset consisted of about six landings down the runway which was terribly embarassing for me and amusing to the people in the back.'

Hope said that when he came back as a tutor in 1971/72 he found the Course much more sophisticated, with governed and turbine-powered helicopters with flight control systems. This has been the way with the School increasingly through the 1970s and into the '80s as the output of the School will be for graduates who will largely be testing such advanced systems in the future.

The Course passed without incident and at the end of the year the students went their separate ways. Again, one of the Course went to Hatfield, after a career within the Service test field. Squadron Leader Pete Smith then went on to Prestwick on the Jetstream. Four immediately served at Boscombe after the Course, with two going to Bedford. Squadron Leader P. Gordon-Johnson, one of the men who went to Aero Flight Bedford, ended up at British Aerospace Warton after his RAF service. The foreigners returned to their respective test establishments in their own countries.

To supplement the Viscounts, the School acquired this Hawker Siddeley Argosy C Mk 1 *XR105* in April 1971, having transferred from the A&AEE fleet. It was this aircraft which suffered the catastrophic fatal crash on the runway on 24 April 1976.

CHAPTER 7
Keeping Abreast of Developments

By the mid-1970s the School was well ensconced at Boscombe, with all the sadnesses over leaving Farnborough dissipated. It had found its feet in the new regime which was the Aeroplane and Armament Experimental Establishment. Now, as it moved forward, its task was to maintain its very high standard of tuition and to adapt this to fit the changing patterns and requirements that were to come as the years rolled by. The first of these developments came in 1973. Robin Hargreaves explained:

'The idea was that test pilots in their working life would be working very closely with Flight Test Engineers, and it was thought that training engineers together with the pilots would greatly improve their working relationships and the efficiency and effectiveness of the teams. It had already been tried at other test pilot schools. In fact the French School, EPNER, had incorporated such training from its inception in 1947. It wasn't new but it was a good idea and the flight test engineers' course started off at ETPS in a small way with just a couple of students, eventually building up to five students by 1976. It worked out practically that there should be one engineer attached to each of the pilot syndicates and that he would be doing very much the same sort of work he would be doing later on when he graduated — to plan a series of trials for a team of two or three pilots, to tape their data,

both from the instrumentation and the verbal debrief, and then write a report using the results from all the pilots in the team. As there were normally three fixed-wing and two rotary-wing syndicates each year the final number of engineers was five but this was only achieved in 1976 and 1979. The plan fell foul of the Civil Service manning situation which, for many years, had run a ban on increasing establishments and this even militated against recruiting a full-time tutor to train these engineers. Consequently the School had to muddle along in typical British fashion by borrowing people for part of their working day to act as part-time tutors, which was not very satisfactory. Because of this and because of the increasing pressure on manpower within the civilians at Boscombe Down, we had to slowly reduce the numbers of engineers that we trained, averaging out at no more than two in the early eighties.'

This new scheme had the effect of bringing back on to the ETPS scene one of its original architects — Maclaren Humphreys. He had by now retired and had taken on a job as Training Careers Advisor and one of the tasks that came his way was to help in the selection of the first Flight Test Engineers to take part in the ETPS Course. He remembers:

'We realised that taking people, even highly qualified people, straight from university or elsewhere without any practical experience of aircraft testing would take anything from two or three years before you could say that you had a fully-trained test engineer. For the sake of giving up one year of his useful employment, you got a fully-trained FTE much earlier.'

With changing requirements there had been slight changes in the style and composition of the School's staff. At the beginning of 1973 it was composed as follows:

Commanding Officer (this title replaced that of Commandant): Group Captain D. P. Hall, AFC, RAF.

Chief Test Flying Instructor: Wing Commander S. W. Bainbridge, AFRAeS, RAF.

Chief Ground Instructor: Squadron Leader J. B. Rodgers, MSc, FCA, FCIMA, FSS, CEng, AFRAeS, RAF.

Senior Fixed-Wing Tutor: Squadron Leader J. E. Watts-Phillips, BSc(Eng), AFRAeS, RAF.

Fixed-Wing Tutors: Squadon Leaders A. A. Clarke, BSc(Eng), ACGI, AFRAeS, RAF, and G. E. Bridges, RAF; and Lieutenant L. L. Ernst, US Navy.

Senior Rotary-Wing Tutor: Squadron Leader J. T. Egginton, AFC, AFRAeS, RAF.

Rotary-Wing Tutor: Lieutenant Commander P. J. G. Harper, RN.

Assistant Ground Instructor: Squadron Leader F. D. Allan, BSc(Tech), MSc, CEng, MIMechE, RAF.

Aerosystems Tutor: Flight Lieutenant R. M. Bayne, RAF.

Qualified Flying Instructor: Squadron Leader M. A. Vickers, AFC, RAF.

Qualified Helicopter Instructor: Flight Lieutenant B. V. Little, RAF.

Senior Air Engineer: Squadron Leader A. E. Risby, RAF.

Air Engineers: Squadon Leader G. Humphrey, RAF, and Flight Lieutenant R. Dockerty, RAF.

Although the School did have its own aircraft, it now relied on the A&AEE to supply certain aircraft for its exercises, and this from time to time caused problems when both organisations needed the same aircraft urgently. On this grey October morning the Boscombe apron contains the ETPS Argosy *XR105*, ETPS Wessex HAS Mk 1 *XS863* and the A&AEE Canberra B Mk 2 *WH876*.

Operations Officer: Flight Lieutenant D. J. Brown, RAF.

Adjutant: Sergeant T. Fleming, RAF.

One of the innovations which had come in since the move back to Boscombe was the interchange, between the various test pilot schools, of pilots as tutors, as exemplified in the list above by Lieutenant Ernst of the US Navy. The Fleet had by now been reduced to seventeen aircraft and three gliders, as follows:

Argosy C 1	*XR105*
Basset CC 1	*XS742, XS743*
	(V-Stab a/c)
Canberra T 4	*WJ865, WJ867*
Chipmunk T 10	*WD321*
Hunter F 6	*XE587, XF375*
Hunter T 7/T 7A	*XL564, XL579, XL616*
Puma HC 1	*XW233*
Scout AH 1	*XR436*
Twin Pioneer CC 2	*XT610*
Wessex HAS1, DB 3	*XS863, XT255*
Whirlwind HAR 10	*XJ409*

Gliders — Rhonsegler K6 *XW640*, Sedbergh TX 1 *WB920*, SKY *XS876*.

It will be seen that the Sea King had disappeared but had been replaced by a Westland Aerospatiale Puma HC 1 which filled the need for a modern, twin-engined helicopter.

To make use of all this expertise came seventeen students to start the 32nd Fixed Wing and 11th Rotary Wing Courses on 1 February 1973. Only six were from the RAF, none from the Navy but one man from the Army Air Corps. Three came from Australia, two from the RAAF and one from the RAN, an Italian, a US Navy man, an Indian, Frenchman, South African and two Germans — one a civilian, the other from the German Navy.

During Don Hall's time as Commanding Officer, the School Film was produced. It was a great success and gave everybody a good idea of the School's operation, the students' tasks and included some magnificent flying shots of inverted spinning in the Hunter. It was shown to each new course when it arrived, and to visitors. In the mid-1970s the School was invited to attend a trade fair in Milan. As none of the School could afford to go, and the Ministry would not pay, no one went; but there was a competition for the best film depicting commercial activities or training so the film was sent. Much to the School's surprise the film won the prize of a trophy as the best film of the trade fair. According to Hall's successor, the trophy was rather ugly and a typical piece of Italian equipment, but it was another pointer to the excellence of the School and looked well on display in the School premises.

Mention of inverted spinning in the Hunter introduces one of ETPS's unique facets. For the majority of swept-wing aircraft spinning is a 'no-go' exercise, but the Hunter is sufficiently tractable for it to be spun and recovered. This means that with this type all the characteristics associated with a swept-wing aircraft departing from controlled flight can be demonstrated to students and exercised by them, a priceless piece of training for which ETPS has become famous.

Before embarking on the actual flying, the theory of spinning is taught in the ground school, together with the pro- and anti-spin variables. Two of the School's Hunter T 7s have been modified with special instrumentation by fitting a head-up spin panel and this is combined with a voice recorder, a paper trace recorder and UHF telemetry, which is monitored on a visual display by a ground-based safety pilot. The spin panel comprises a turn needle, roll lights, angle of attack indicator, and altitude, elevator, rudder and aileron positions. There is also an audio-visual warning system instructing the pilot to recover at 20,000 ft (6,100 m) and eject at 10,000 ft (3,030 m). The telemetry records all control positions as well as altitude,

airspeed, angle of attack and roll and yaw rates to the safety pilot who can give verbal assistance to the pilot if necessary.

A normal sortie involves six or seven spins and the programme starts with incipient spins leading to inverted spins, including spins with intentional mishandling. This involves the application of in-spin and out-spin aileron and the effects on the handling. For most of the students it will have been a long time since they have done any spinning so it comes as a most interesting exercise. But its value to the testing world is that it teaches pilots how to enter uncontrolled flight, some of the characteristics of such flight, and methods of reacting in such conditions.

Harry Nelson, who was on the 1974 Course, had this to say about spinning the Hunters:

'It is a particularly interesting spin mode on an aircraft. I had done a lot of spinning before on the Jet Provost and I was quite happy with the principles of spinning, but I had never flown a swept-wing aircraft through a spin. Funnily enough, flying the aeroplane was in some ways the least difficult part; it was a relief to get airborne and actually fly the spins. The far more difficult job, to my mind, was actually monitoring the exercise from the telemetry hut — you worked as a team. The instrument panel scan in the hut was completely different to that in the aeroplane and you had a key role to play if things were going wrong — you could order the guy to eject and certainly advise him that he hadn't got proper controls on, for example. I found it more difficult to sit there with someone else flying a spin than I did flying the aeroplane myself.'

The Hunter spinning exercises have remained one of the most valuable parts of the course. These graphic stills from a film sequence show Hunter T Mk 7 XL612 entering into an inverted spin.

For the 1974 Course Don Hall handed over command to Group Captain H. A. Merriman, CBE, AFC (now Air Vice-Marshal). Wally Bainbridge remained as Chief Test Flying Instructor. Nineteen students went through the Course, of which two were Flight Test Engineers. One RN, one AAC and eight RAF officers made up the British contingent of pilots with one each from France, Germany, Australia, Italy, India and the US Navy. The aircraft complement remained the same for this course (No 33 Fixed Wing and No 12 Rotary Wing).

Harry Nelson, who had come to the Course from instructing on Jet Provosts and then a tour captaining Vulcans, had applied for the 1973 Course but was turned down on account of his maths, or lack of it. When he re-applied for 1974 John Rodgers, who interviewed him on the academic side, said: 'Well, I've got to congratulate you, you have improved your maths this year — you've doubled your last year's results. This year you've managed fourteen per cent!' After re-sitting the maths before starting he was accepted and passed the Course. Having always flown in twin-seat or bigger aircraft he recounts an amusing incident on the Course:

'I had been flying the Hunter F 6 over a period of some weeks and became increasingly concerned because I couldn't find the intercom switch — this went on and on and I became acutely embarrassed by it. The radio seemed to work all right but I still couldn't find the switch. Eventually, out of sheer frustration, I walked into the crew room one day with the tutors and other students and said "Come on, I give in, where is the intercom switch on the Hunter F 6?" Everybody burst out laughing because, being a single-seater, there isn't one. They had been waiting for the first guy to make a fool of himself and ask, but all the other students sitting around the crew room breathed a sigh of relief because none of them had found it either!'

It was during this Course that the dear old Twin Pioneer bit the dust. Harry Nelson was again in on this — flying it with Flight Lieutenant John Bishop, whose exercise it was. The exercise consisted of assessment of its operational short take-off and landing capabilities. It was flown on the grass airfield at nearby Andover and the Pilots' Notes said: 'Hold the tailwheel firmly on the ground with fully up elevators whilst running up to full power then release the brakes and push the stick forward to get the tail up and lift of'. Twice John Bishop nearly put the nose in and when the aircraft returned to Boscombe for a running change they handed over to John Watkins, the US Navy student, and Evangelisti the Italian Air Force man. What John Bishop and Harry had nearly done these two accomplished, getting the aircraft's nose firmly stuck in Andover's grass. On bringing it back to Boscombe it was found that the ballast normally present in the rear of the fuselage had been removed the previous weekend for parachuting and not replaced, so everyone's reputations were saved! The Twin Pin was repaired and in service again within a week but before the next Course arrived it was sold to a civilian outfit.

Harry Nelson remembers, that on this Course they decided in the evenings to improve the understanding between the foreign nationals and the home team by having national meals. The English couple produced a full roast beef dinner, the Indians — the Yadavs — laid on a most splendid Indian meal, the one at the Australians' house involved mainly Fosters beer, and so on. Harry went on to RAE Bedford after the Course and is now a test pilot at British Aerospace, Woodford. John Bishop remained in the Service test flying scene, serving at Farnborough and Bedford. John Bolton was another on this Course who remained within the Service sphere and who was, until recently, Commanding Officer at ETPS himself. Two others went to Farnborough, Flight Lieutenant I. E. Frost, who then returned to the 'sharp end' of the Air Force, and Flight Lieutenant J. M. O'Dwyer who was killed in an asymmetric accident to a Meteor at Farnborough on 14 February 1975. Also killed flying soon after was the Indian student, Flight Lieutenant D. Yadav.

Two new trophies appeared in the ETPS Lists for 1974. One was the Dunlop Trophy which was presented to the best Flight Test Engineer and was won by Mr J. L. F. Denning. The other trophy has an interesting history. It was originally cast in June 1928, being a silver model of a Short Singapore II flying-boat. It was presented to Sir Alan Cobham and his wife in commemoration of their epic circuit of Africa flight in 1927 in such a flying-boat. Sir Alan's son, Michael Cobham, presented it to the School, to be known as the 'Sir Alan Cobham Award', and to be given annually to the student who consistently demonstrated the highest standard of flying in all aspects of the Course.

Alan Merriman's tenure of command was marked by continual battles with Whitehall for the continued effective existence of the School. The pressure to reduce the overhead costs of the School was intense and never-ceasing. One of the problems was that of making clear to civil servants, divorced from the flying scene, the reasons why so few students needed so many aeroplanes. It was hard for them to realise that a large variety of types was needed by the very nature of the training being given. It was not long into 1970 before Merriman was told that the School must make a percentage reduction in its fleet and in this instance the order was to reduce numbers, not actual finance. So

after a long look and with very many regrets, it was decided that the Chipmunk and the gliders would be offered up as a sacrifice. This happened and the 1974 Course was the last one to enjoy the benefits of weekend gliding. Thus, one of ETPS's long-standing traditions finally came to an end; it was one of the major losses from the point of view of the great experience it gave to many of the students who had never flown gliders before. Cost was a further reason for the departure of the Twin Pioneer, a unique aircraft which could not really be replaced. It was eventually replaced, in September 1975, by an Andover which was given up by Farnborough and this had the advantage of providing another turboprop type and a more suitable passenger aircraft for use on the visits to industry and elsewhere, for the loss of the two Viscounts had been felt.

Merriman realised that it was not only aircraft that were under attack in the mid-1970s. There was considerable controversy about the number of students, since the requirements for UK students were falling off as the amount of new aircraft coming into service was dropping. The School had an obligation to take in two students a year (one from France and one from the US Navy) and the British requirement was getting down to five or six students, whereas the School was trying to maintain a student population of about fourteen. Thus it was necessary to encourage more overseas students, and this raised the question in financial circles as to whether the latter were paying their way. At one time it could be made to look that the School was being run for the benefit of the foreign students and the question came up of eliminating the School altogether and training the small British input at the French or American schools. However, it was clear that these Schools were not designed to train test pilots to British methods appropriate to the British test establishments and, in any case, there was no guarantee that the overseas schools would continue in existence or whether their charges would go up. In the end, the overriding factor for maintaining ETPS was that it was a tremendous advertisement for Britain and all that it stood for in terms of advanced technology, technical training and the edge that ETPS had over any other establishments, which was recognised worldwide.

During Merriman's time, with the incorporation of Engineering training as well, both the syllabus and aircraft were adapted as test flying generally took an even bigger swing in the direction of flight systems. New aircraft were in the pipeline for the School which would enable this to be flown more realistically, but in the meantime the syllabus was adjusted to give more flight system assessments and fewer on the pure handling side; some of the latter, which were simply sorties for gathering numerical data for reduction to tables, were abandoned. It was an altogether different scene from the days when Sammy Wroath set the School up on the south side of the airfield. But there was still one outpost of the School on the south side. This was the rotary-wing emporium, which was cloistered with A&AEE's 'D' Squadron. This militated against the cohesion of the School with the rest of it being on the north side of the runway. Contact between the two was intermittent, often resulting in a fifteen-minute wait to cross the runway. This problem of physical division of the School's buildings still has not been solved.

As the School had been shrinking (it no longer had its own engineering staff, nor its own Mess) it hardly justified having a Group Captain in command but the School was reluctant to tell the outside world that it had shrunk to such dimensions that it only warranted a Wing Commander! However, ways were found around this and eventually, two COs later, the Group Captain post was combined with that of

Superintendent of Flying at Boscombe Down, the incumbent having to be someone who had good experience of the School. This was accomplished in Mike Adams' time who went on to become Superintendent of Test Flying and Training, which was the new title.

For the Courses in 1975 (No 34 FW, No 13 RW and No 2 FTE) the RAF provided eight students, and the RN one. Overseas input was one from Australia, two Italians, two German civilians, the customary French and US Navy people, another Yadav from India and a Danish Air Force officer. Four flight test engineers appeared, one a rotary-wing man and three fixed-wing to work, each one, with a fixed-wing syndicate. Changes in the aircraft fleet were minor, different Hunters and a 'new' Lightning T 5 in place of the second prototype two-seater. During the Course the Andover arrived in September and the prototype Jet Provost T 5 made a most useful addition to the fleet. There was still the problem of a permanent tutor for the Flight Test Engineers but the task was carried out by an old stalwart of Boscombe, Terry Heffernan.

At the end of 1975 Group Captain Merriman was promoted to become Commandant of Boscombe Down and Group Captain M. K. Adams, AFC, took his place for the next year before, as already mentioned, the Group Captain posts at Boscombe Down were combined. Quite a few changes took place in the fleet during the year. A Wessex HC 2 arrived for the beginning of the Course in 1976 but was bent in March and replaced by a Wessex HU 5. More importantly, what had been planned some years ago began to come to fruition in this year. For the first time, new aircraft had been ordered specifically for the School. The purchase was two two-seat Jaguar T Mk 2s and the first of these arrived during July, the second the following year. These were most valuable tools for the School as they were far in advance of anything else on the unit in terms of modern methods and equipment, but especially in systems which was what was needed so much.

Despite the fact that the School regularly operated its aircraft to the very corners of their performance envelopes, it had a remarkable safety record with no accidents for eight years. This all went by the board in 1976 and for no apparent reason. The first took place almost before the Course had started on 22 January 1976 when Hunter T 7 *XL579* had a total engine failure whilst downwind to land. In no way could it be got on to the airfield so the two crew (one was the US Navy exchange tutor, Walt Honor) ejected. Then in March the Wessex HC 2 which had just arrived was written off in a very heavy landing, again with no loss of life. But on 24 April the Argosy, whilst engaged in a two-engine out overshoot, went out of control into a small spinney at the side of the runway and burnt. The Italian student, Captain Giuseppe Puglisi, and the Flight Engineer, Terry Colgan, were killed and the QFI, the incorrigible Mike Vickers, got out with a broken leg and several other fractures. He was flying again within weeks, probably still in plaster! His attitude to flying was that if he did not get five trips a day he was hard done by.

Wally Bainbridge had left as CTFI and his place was taken by Wing Commander J. A. Robinson, AFC, who had done the Course in 1962, been back as a tutor in 1969, and now took on the Chief Instructor rôle. Within a year the Commandant had become part of the total Boscombe set-up and the Chief Instructor, in effect, became CO of the School. The old idea of the CTFI looking after the flying training only, and the CGI the ground school, was gone — the Chief Instructor now headed it all up which resulted in the Principal Tutor being given much more responsibility and so on down the line.

Courses Nos 35 (FW), 14 (RW) and 3 (FTE) comprised twenty-one students of which five were Flight Test Engineers, including an Israeli Air Force Captain and a Hindustan Aircraft engineer. Quite a spread came from overseas with the usual US Navy man, a Canadian, Indian, two Australians, French Navy, two Israeli Air Force men, a Swedish Army man, and the Italian who was killed in the Argosy. Five RAF and two RN pilots made up the Course.

Lieutenant de V. Paul Habert was the French Navy pilot and he gives us some interesting insights into the reactions of foreign students:

'I didn't ask to go to ETPS — I wanted to do the test job so I applied for a posting to the French CEV mainly because I thought I could be posted in the South of France; coming from Brittany I was looking to the south. As soon as I had been posted to CEV I found a house in the south then my new boss told me I was going to England and there was nothing I could do about it. So when I arrived I was not very happy about it at first.

'Everyone in France is supposed to speak English perfectly well so I was not very worried about the language problem, but when I arrived and started talking English nobody was understanding what I was saying! Also I had never heard an Englishman speak English before so I had great difficulties to understand the way people were talking. But everybody was so friendly and helpful that after a month I could cope with everything except the telephone English. Fortunately I was staying near Ian Gonsal, one of the Australians, and he decided to teach me English. After a while I was also able to distinguish between the different accents.

'When I applied to CEV the most

Normally the School, for economic reasons, had to gather its fleet from aircraft no longer needed by the Services or the other research establishments. However, in 1976 and 1977 the fruits of good housekeeping arrived in the shape of two two-seat Jaguar T Mk 2 trainers, especially ordered for ETPS. Sadly, both have since been lost, *XX916* in 1981 and *XX915* in 1984.

exciting thing for me was to be able to fly multi-engined aircraft with a crew. As I had to wait in France some three months before coming to England I got some experience in but the crew were not helpful. In England the first flight I made with a crew was a big difference because they were very helpful and very nice; they were always trying to help me if I had trouble speaking on the radio or trying to find a switch or understanding the check list. I was very impressed with the Argosy, and really it was a big thing to fly. I was very proud that after six months in England they allowed me to go alone with that big aircraft, in charge of a trainee and the flight engineer. It was like doing the watch on the bridge of a ship, you even had to climb a ladder to get up to the cockpit.

'I was a bit surprised at the beginning to see how people seemed to be concerned about winning a trophy since the beginning of the Course.

During the coffee break in the morning there was always somebody standing in front of the big list in the ground school, trying to see which trophy they would win! I didn't feel concerned at the beginning but in the summer, when I made a good report and everyone was talking about it, I say, well maybe, I could win something but, of course, I was not thinking about the McKenna at all. That was certainly too difficult for a non-English speaking student. At the end of the Course when I understood that I was in a good position to win it I put in much work and I was very proud to win it, and I was very happy to see that the other students and tutors were happy with me. Maybe elsewhere people would have been jealous but in the School, nobody.

'Of the aircraft, one of the most impressive was the Lightning; even coming from a fighter squadron I was surprised at my first trip. After take-off I forgot to take the undercarriage up because everything was rushing so quickly, but we had to bring back the speed to get it up before starting to climb which was really impressive. The worst aircraft was the Canberra because it was really uncomfortable and you can't see anything outside. I used to say that it was really a flying submarine and perhaps it was better to fly it without seeing outside.

'I flew the Jaguar for my Preview exercise and we went to Lossiemouth for two weeks. I was in a syndicate with an English pilot, an Israeli pilot and an Israeli engineer. Both Israelis were very interested at that time because the Egyptians were planning to buy the Jaguar and so they did a tremendous amount of work, trying to see what its good and bad points were and how they could be beaten in some sort of way. At the end, the Flight Test Engineer said: "Well, now they can buy the Jaguar, I know what to do if they have it!" It was helpful to me, too, when I came back to CEV and had to fly the Jaguar myself.'

Flight Lieutenant John Rochfort was one of the RAF students on the Course. He did not consider himself one of the bright boys — he thought that most aviators would love to be a test pilot. 'It's a great ego trip. (Cor, that would be really smooth. I could wear tight jeans and drive a fast motor car and be a test pilot); then the sensible bit comes over — that you have to be pretty good, above average — have a degree in moon landing or a fearsome brain — and that puts everybody off.' He was at Valley instructing on Gnats and so he devised a scheme with a colleague to visit all the establishments ('we could easily get aeroplanes and float around the Air Force') and talk to the people involved in test flying. Eventually he was called for an interview:

'It is a very daunting experience — the Ground School quizzing becomes you versus him and the blackboard; then you get idiotic questions out of *Aviation Week* hurled at you and you field those as best you can. Finally, there is the big board which is fairly high-powered — in-depth questions by senior officers as to why you are still a Flight Lieutenant!

As to the flying, he really enjoyed the pure handling exercises; and as to spinning the Hunter: 'I enjoyed that because invariably as soon as the thing goes upside down there is a lot of negative "g" on and yaw rate is high. The net result is that within about a turn and a half I wouldn't know which way I was up and had no idea what to do next. It always used to amuse me that my brain completely stopped working — completely finished, big saucer-shaped eyes staring out of the window, wondering what on earth I was doing there, but enjoying it.'

One of the aspects of ETPS which he found so different to the RAF was the approach, so important in test flyng, that the known answer was not always the only one. He found himself ill at ease with the Canberra; to quote him:

'The Canberra is a silly aeroplane — it is a very physical one and with one engine cut it requires a lot of physical effort to regain control of it or retain control of it and, bearing in mind that I'm essentially a single-seat, single-engine person (ignore the Lightning — that's basically one engine as far as handling is concerned), this asymmetric business was totally new to me, and the worst of the lot was the Canberra. She is quite a rude aeroplane if you treat her wrongly. If you get the speed too low, start playing around with power or the flaps, or the undercarriage at the wrong time, you put yourself in an unrecoverable situation, which used to grab my attention a bit! I felt most uneasy about it and what I liked about the Course was that — I don't know what they thought at the time — (they, being the staff; Pete, Duncan and mates, who were looking after me), but I do recall going up to them and saying "I'm not at all happy with the Canberra, I feel that it's winning every time — can I go off on my own and sort it out?" "Yes, off you go," which I thought was wizard, because that's what I wanted to do. I didn't want someone to come up and say "This is how you do it, this is what you must do." They had already done that. I wanted to go off and practice it — this business of being a slow learner if you like; also knowing your limitations!'

He found, as almost all students find, that after the intensive activity of the Course, the change to actual test flying is an anti-climax indeed. Inevitably at Boscombe Down, Bedford and Farnborough, each test flight is liable to be followed by two or three weeks of altering the bits and pieces and the pace is very slow and involves endless cups of coffee in the crew room and waiting for the boffins to get the equipment or aircraft up to scratch.

John's views on the industry visits were quite succinct. 'The curly sandwiches and bottled beer at Westland — fascinating. The Dowty-Rotol lot, which is a bustling, dynamic outfit. Ferranti, that's always good, they are the royal hosters. I think it is a very important part of the Course and reinforces your understanding of the industry.'

Ian Gonsal was one of the Australians on No 35 Course. For the RAAF personnel it was not a case of applying for a test pilots' course, they were selected by their postings people, just as any other posting, and depending on the requirements at ARDU (the Aircraft Research and Development Unit) at Laverton to which they all go on completion of the Course. It was Ian

who helped the Frenchman, Paul Habert, to learn English; he also tells of Giuseppe Puglisi, the Italian, a story about his interpretation of English:

'Guiseppe had done transonic handling in the Canberra where, as you accelerate to Mach you come to about Mach. 79 and the rudders start "tramping" (the in-word to describe the rudder pedals vibrating from side to side). In his report Giuseppe had written that he "approached Mach. 79, the Mach number at knee trembling" and Pete Sedgwick's red ink comment was "Don't let this get out, Giuseppe, or you will have people queuing up to fly the Canberra", and poor old Giuseppe could not understand what the joke was.'

It seems that ground school hits all the students hard. Ian Gonsal records:

'My initial impression of ground school was like trying to drink from an overflowing water hydrant. You can only open your mouth so much and a lot of it goes down by the side! There's no doubt about it that the first three weeks of ground school were a bit mind blowing, but you just had to take in as much as you could. Again I surprised myself. I thought it would be completely over my head but instead of it being beyond my reasoning capacity I found it just hard work to take it all in, remember it and blurt it all out at the end.'

He also remarked, that in some of the more energetic exercises (eg Hunter spinning) you are supposed to speak into the tape recorder the readings of 'g', rate of rotation, altitude, etc, but when you play the tape back to write your report all you hear is heavy breathing! One of the irritations he found about the Course was that the students spent so much time doing exercises to establish limits and faults on aircraft but never, inevitably, did any flying to try and find answers. Naturally, this would be impossible on the Course because of time limitations; once the graduates get into the test flying scene and find out how long such fault eradication takes, it becomes apparent why this is not a feature of the Course.

With the Course over, the foreigners returned to their respective countries; one of the Israelis, Major Amiram Shaked, was killed soon after. The Canadian, Bob Auld, came back later to Boscombe on an exchange posting to 'D' Squadron for helicopter test flying.

The year had seen quite a depletion of aircraft, not only as a result of accidents; the first of the two Bassets had been struck off charge and scrapped and the Hunter T 7A returned to A&AEE. Before the next Course started the last remaining Whirlwind helicopter was also retired. To balance this up the second Jaguar T 2 arrived in January and a DB Sea King in July. This was Robbie Robinson's last year as Chief Instructor and the incoming students comprised eighteen, of which three were Flight Test Engineers, two from the MOD establishments and yet another Israeli. The British complement was thin on pilots, just two RAF, three RN and one from the AAC. The overseas contribution included the 'regulars': US Navy, RAAF, Italian, Canadian and Indian, to which were added a Dutchman and a South African.

It had been a good year, despite accidents. One student commented:

> 'On the staff side, again, my impression of ETPS as a Course, as distinct from any other course I have been on, I thought it had the best staff/student relationship I have ever seen. We felt, and we were made to feel (if I were on the staff I would hope that I could make my students feel the same) that we were all graduate operational pilots, we were picked to come to ETPS because of attributes which were usually assessed as above average — at least in flying ability. There was enough hard work at ETPS and there was enough self-generated work at ETPS and enough, not self-criticism, but it gets easier as the year goes on to know that you are not doing right, to know that you are misassessing something, that the staff do not need to hound you — in my opinion on my year, we were not hounded. The guidelines were very clear, that is, we were expected to hand in our reports ten days after the day of the last flight. We could expect that report to be critically reviewed and marked and we could expect to be debriefed on how we assessed the aeroplane in a particular way that had been done many times before and, not so much there was a book answer, but there were some fairly well known and fairly well reasoned recommendations that we could expect to make at this assessment. I was very pleased with the staff/student relationship both at work and socially.'

By contrast with the previous year the Course proceeded without mishap, proving that ETPS's modus operandi was basically sound. Two of the Course in 1977 have since gone into the British Aircraft Industry, Flight Lieutenant R. A. Cowpe to Rolls-Royce at Bristol and Flight Lieutenant C. F. Roberts to British Aerospace at Dunsfold. At the end of the year Robbie Robinson, looking back at his periods with ETPS, recalled meeting six Courses and 'each Course had a character of its own. You can always remember the idiosyncrasies of each Course, one being smooth, another being trouble. I think the staff always liked a Course which caused them a bit of trouble because there was a bit more spirit in it. The character of a Course is set by only three or four people, the ring leaders.'

At the Battle of Britain Cocktail Party that year Tony Blackman, Chief Test Pilot at Woodford, was enquiring about a pilot to join his team. This often happens to the boss of ETPS and in the end Robinson took the job himself and went on to become Chief Test Pilot.

In the wings was Wing Commander J. E. Watts-Phillips, BSc, MRAeS, who came along and took over the rôle of Chief Instructor for the next tour. Also returning to ETPS for the 1978 Courses as Principal Rotary Wing Tutor was Squadron Leader Martin Mayer, AFC:

> 'I was immediately surprised to see the difference in the Rotary Wing Course. It was both better disciplined and better structured, having a closer grip on the actual pattern of exercises, and their content had increased considerably. We now had a lot of instruction on stability and the effects of auto-pilots and twin-engined operations.'

Mayer mentions the change of structure and this, of course, had been part of the change in syllabus and emphasis in the Ground School. At this time it was providing some 300 hours of lectures by both the School's staff and visitors from industry and the Services. After the first three weeks, which is all ground school, the student then spends an hour or two on ground lectures each morning before moving on to the flying side, aiming to provide the theoretical side of the afternoon's exercise. Visual aids to this now included an analogue computer and a cathode ray oscillograph. The computer could be linked to an aircraft model to demonstrate dynamic behaviour. By now there was a specific Aerosystems Tutor to take care of this growing side of the Course and he had, for the fixed-wing students, an inertial nav/attack simulator with a head-up display, similar to the Harrier's, and a ground rig of the Jaguar's NAVWASS. For the rotary-wing students there was a TANS system, which was progressively being installed in all the helicopters. The flying

Being at Boscombe Down, the School had the advantage of the servicing facilities persuant to this research establishment. ETPS's Lightning T 4 in the Weighbridge hangar.

Another very valuable asset of the School was Beagle Basset CC Mk 1 *XS743* which, in the early seventies, was converted into a variable stability demonstrator.

syllabus, now designed to cover the three different departments of Handling, Performance and Systems, used the aircraft fleet in the following way:

Sepecat Jaguar T 2 *XX915, XX916*
   used for manoeuvre boundaries and systems assessments

BAC Lightning T 5 *XS422*
   supersonic handling

Hawker Hunter F 6 *XE587, XF375*
Hawker Hunter T 7 *XL564, XL612*
   subsonic handling and spinning

Hawker Siddeley Andover C 1 *XS606*
   large aircraft handling

BAC Canberra T 4 *WJ867*
   asymmetric handling

Beagle Basset CC 1 *XS743*
   variable stability characteristics

Westland Sea King HAS 1 *XV370*
   large aircraft handling and systems assessment

Westland Wessex HAS 3 *XT255*
   engine handling and automatic flying control systems

Westland Gazelle HT 3 *XZ936*
   flight envelope exploration and stability

The latter aircraft, straight off the Westland production line, was added to the fleet during 1978 and became an integral part of the fleet, replacing the long-suffering Westland Scout.

For the 1978 Courses seventeen students turned up. Sadly, there were only two Flight Test Engineers, both fixed-wing, Mr R. N. Burton, a Boscombe man, and Lieutenant D. Benedetti of the Italian Air Force of the RSV, who took the Dunlop Trophy. In addition to the customary foreign students, there was Captain A. Ridzwan of the Royal Malaysian Air Force and Herr H. P. Weger from the helicopter company, Messerschmitt-Bolkow-Blohm. There were only six British Service pilots, three RAF, two RN and one AAC. Germany provided a man from the Kriegsmarine rather than the customary Luftwaffe.

Squadron Leader Martin Mayer found that the Course itself had changed markedly:

'Of course, there were far more exciting designs in the pipeline than there had been eight years before when I was a student, so it was a very exciting time. We had six students between the two tutors, which made it quite hard work, but at about that time we gained a QHI — the fixed-wing people had had a QFI for several years back — and he obviously provided a very good basic teaching on flying the aircraft, which off-loaded the tutors, a great help and got rid of the basic learning that you had to start off with when teaching students. It still didn't get round some of the problems. I can remember we had an Indian student, a delightful chap and, as was my wont whenever the new students arrived, I looked through their log books, and I found that he had a Master Green Instrument Rating. I thought: that's great, because it was one less thing to have to worry about — he could instrument fly on helicopters, which some people find quite difficult.

'I had him in for an interview and mentioned the Master Green IR and asked him how much instrument flying he had done — actual instrument flying in cloud. He said "None". I said "Well, how can you have a MGIR?" and he said "We just look at the instruments and fly the Hip (Russian aircraft), which he had been flying in India. They didn't even use a visor to cover up the outside world. When you have done that for so many hours you get your Master Green". Well, of course, that was just the start of the problem of trying to teach him proper instrument flying in cloud, and he never did hack it to the end of the Course — it was almost impossible for him to do.'

An innovation brought in at this time, towards the end of the Course, was the tour of European Flight Test Centres. Staff and students would climb aboard the Andover and go first to Practica di Mare, Rome, where the RSV would show them test pilots in their own environment and allow them to fly some of their types. After a day or two there, they moved on to the

Another aeronautical oddity which served valuably with the School was this Scottish Aviation Twin Pioneer, XT610. It had interesting flying characteristics and wickerwork passenger seats — quaint.

After long service, the original Lightning was replaced by a standard T Mk 5, *XS422*, and this continued the supersonic role with the School to the mid-eighties.

French CEV at Istres and then on to Manching, the German test centre where the same procedure would follow. In this way a survey of the European test scene would be obtained with a chance to fly new and different types of aircraft. This system has been continued subsequently as a valuable part of the Course.

Missing from the Course from now on were the Indian students. Whilst Wing Commander Bainbridge was CTFI, earlier in the 1970s, the Indian Air Force had sent a delegation to ETPS to see how the School was administered and in 1976 the IAF set up its own school. However, in 1979 another Malaysian came along and two more Israelis, so there was no shortage of foreign students to accompany the five British pilots and three Flight Test Engineers. One of the Israelis was an FTE, as also was Lieutenant U. Vecchi of the Italian Air Force who, at the end of the Course, went back to Italy with the Edwards Award — the first FTE to take

away what had hitherto been the prerogative of the pilot students. This was the last time that the School had its full complement of five Flight Test Engineers; since then the number has tailed off. The fleet remained much the same. An additional Lightning T 5 came within the purview of the School for the latter part of the year and remained for two years. A Westland Sioux AH 1 joined the fleet, too, for a short while. This came about as Martin Mayer describes:

'One thing we realised with the modern helicopters was that many of the handling problem areas had been ironed out on the more sophisticated helicopters. We could not demonstrate retreating blade stall, jack stall and tail rotor stall amongst other things on these types. We needed some sort of aircraft on which we could demonstrate these "nasties" and our eyes turned towards the

Sioux, many of which were going to be sold on the open market for between five and ten thousand pounds each. Of course, the request was turned down on cost grounds. We continued discussions and arguments and eventually the convincing argument was that the acquisition of a Sioux would save costly hours on the Sea King and Lynx (when it came). So the Sioux came and was an extremely good little tool for demonstrating all the basics. But it was a joint user aircraft, shared with 'D' Squadron, and it had only been at Boscombe just over a year when a 'D' Squadron pilot wrote it off. Of

course, it was never replaced as such, although at the end of 1979 a Scout was acquired.'

During this time the requirement had been steadily working up for new aircraft and eventually more new aircraft were ordered for the School; no fewer than three British Aerospace Hawk T 1s, and these were eagerly awaited. The School was still under attack from the Treasury and one of their new tactics was to reduce the cost of the School by reducing the Course length from ten and a half months to four or five months, on the argument that new aircraft coming into service were monochrome in character and therefore only those characteristics applicable

In the mid-seventies the School improved its sartorial elegance by going in for bright orange flying suits, not just for show but for visibility in the case of baling out or ditching in the Channel. Lieutenant Commander Peter Harper, rotary-wing tutor, is briefing his student prior to take-off in Scout AH Mk 1 *XR436*.

to, say, the Tornado needed teaching. Fortunately, the School could counter that the majority of students were now from overseas and their costs were providing the major funding of the School so that the Ministry of Defence were, in fact, getting their test pilots on the cheap. Because the overseas candidates would be flying such a wide variety of aircraft, the present Course needed to be maintained. In any case, such a short Course would turn out a very poor type of test pilot. The other, increasing, argument was, and is, that all these active contacts with so many overseas air forces provided a vast fund of contact for overseas military sales of aircraft and equipment, a point which is increasingly cogent. Through the 1970s the pattern had been changed sufficiently to take the School into the '80s and so there was no change for the Course coming in 1980. Numbers for Nos 39, 18 and 7 Courses were down to fifteen, just three engineers, three RAF officers and two RN, together with US Navy, French, Australian, German and Italian students.

It was not only the fixed-wing flying that was spectacular. Martin Mayer comments:

'Perhaps the most hairy experience that was done on TPS on the helicopters was lever delay exercises, which required flying along, chopping the engine or both engines simultaneously and seeing how long you could leave the lever up before you actually ran out of rotor rpm — and this was a very finely judged exercise. It was all right at sixty knots in level flight, where you perhaps had three or four seconds to lower the lever, but I remember in the Wessex we used to finish up in a climb (a max power climb) at twenty knots, chopping both engines, and the rate of rotor rpm drop was fantastic. You barely had half a second before you had to slam the lever down,

which meant that two pilots had to do it. One chopped the engines and the other immediately lowered the lever and it was a very convincing exercise to show how quick you had to be in losing power and getting the lever down and the aircraft into auto-rotation. The sort of things that students would never do in the Services and a very good example of the sort of lesson you could learn on TPS and nowhere else.'

As the Course came to a close the title of the School's boss was changed from Chief Instructor to Commanding Officer, coming back full circle to the original title back in 1943. The holder of that title, Wing Commander Watts-Phillips, was tour-expired and handed over to Wing Commander Robin Hargreaves, BSc, MRAeS. He had done his test pilot training at EPNER, the French school, in 1965/66 and it was amusing that during his reign at ETPS his opposite number at EPNER was a graduate of ETPS! This made for an even closer liaison than usual.

During 1981 the fleet again saw some changes. With great joy the three Hawks were received between May and July and were assimilated towards the end of the Course. One by one they went into Boscombe's hangar to be instrumented, making them different to the standard aircraft in RAF service. There are good reasons for this instrumentation, a certain amount of which is incorporated in all the ETPS fleet.

All modern aircraft undergoing flight trials will, in any case, carry some instrumentation for recording purposes, in addition to those instruments being installed to supply the pilot himself with information about the progress of the flight and, in certain conditions such as spinning, the exact position of his controls; this becomes even more essential in the new generation of fly-by-wire aircraft. Also, in modern trials aircraft, the controls are wired for telemetry to a ground station giving information to the ground observers of the real-time situation in the air. All this needs to be built into the training programme at ETPS so that pilots will be able to participate fully in such programmes when they graduate.

To accomplish these ends on the Hawks, various features were incorporated. Externally, airstream direction detector vanes were added to the pitot head and an outside air temperature probe to the port side of the nose. Within the cockpit there are additional displays across the top of both front and rear coamings with instruments showing control positions, control forces, angle of attack and side-slip. In the centre position, normally occupied by the Hawk's gunsight, a special spin panel can be fitted, or alternatively a special package for teaching performance flight testing. On the port side the weapons control panel has been replaced by a fuel flow-meter and fuel remaining indicator. An additional UHF radio is fitted which is largely used in connection with the telemetry.

The most important part of the new instrumentation system is the MODAS, the Modular Data Acquisition System, which is a digital tape system located in the baggage compartment. This tape deck records vital aircraft parameters at the rate of sixty times per second for an entire flight of one-and-a-quarter hour's duration. All this information is analysed after the flight by a ground computer and given to the student as a computer print-out. It can also be given to the ground via telemetry link during high-risk exercises such as spinning, coming up on a visual display console similar to that used with the Hunters so, again, a safety pilot can monitor the exercises and, if necessary, give the pilot safety instructions. This is linked in the Hawk to an advanced voice warning system in the aircraft whereby height cues give the student clear worded advice, culminating with the ultimate statement, 'If not recovered, eject'.

The Hawks provided a great fillip to the fixed-wing courses, being brand-new aircraft and having such potential for subsonic use. Very soon they were pressed into some of the spinning exercises, taking the pressure off the increasingly elderly but willing Hunters. The second Lightning, which had been on loan, left the School before the Course resumed in February and the old Wessex HAS 1 was retired in September. Unfortunately, one of the two Jaguars was lost on 24 July 1981 into the Bristol Channel as a result of a bird strike; the pilot was recovered but the navigator drowned. Another unfortunate accident, not on the School, was the death in an Aermacchi MB326 of Captain R. Giola of the Italian Air Force, who had only just graduated from ETPS the previous December.

The 1981 Courses, Nos 40 (Fixed-Wing), 19 (Rotary Wing) and 8 (Flight Test Engineer) included the first USAF student for many a year, Captain L. B. Hammond Jr, a Dutchman and another Malaysian, together with the steady stream from Italy, Germany, France and Australia. One RN, two RAF and two AAC pilots made up the British contingent together with just one of Boscombe's Flight Test Engineers.

For some considerable time ETPS had been exchanging tutors with the US Navy test pilots school at Patuxent River. This was a regular ongoing exchange, of benefit to both Services. In 1981 the US Navy tutor who came to Boscombe was Lieutenant Commander Keith Crawford and he stayed for three years, rather than the customary two which is the duty span in the US Navy. He was in no doubt about the advantages of coming to ETPS as a tutor. He said:

'It became known that the billet over here at ETPS is an extremely desirable one — in fact the best flying job the US Navy has to offer! This is because the School at Boscombe Down still

Another, and major step forward in capabilities took place in 1981 with the acquisition of three brand-new Hawker Siddeley Hawk T Mk 1s, *XX341–3*. These have been able to take over the roles played for so many years by the Hunters as well as incorporating more modern expertise and equipment. One of these, *XX341*, has already been turned into a much more advanced variable stability platform to augment the good work done by the V-S Basset.

flies aeroplanes and conducts the test establishment like we used to at Patuxent River but, since that time, for various reasons including flight safety, we have pared down what the pilots can do and we don't maintain currency in such a wide r nge on as many types as we used to. The USN TPS fleet tends to be very much tactical, carrier-based orientated small aircraft — we don't operate any big aeroplanes to any extent. At ETPS we go further into the supersonic regime with the Lightning than at Pax, where the only transonic aircraft they have is the T-38. Also, I think flying in the UK has a reputation of being more flexible and free as far as what you can do in an aeroplane, pilots getting more responsibility than sometimes we enjoy in the States: we are much more radar-controlled in the States than here in the UK.

'As far as the exercises, what we require the students to do with the data they acquire and the reports they write are almost identical. The main value of the exchange is to continuously compare test techniques and keep up with current developments in that area but from time to time there are other benefits. For example, the US Navy is buying the Hawk for the VTX programme so the opportunity for some of us to be here getting experience on the Hawk (and exploring its flight envelope) will be very valuable, a benefit to the Navy in very concrete terms.'

Into 1982, and an era came to an end with the retirement of the Canberra from ETPS service. The type had first come to the School in the mid-1950s and had served as a most useful training vehicle, albeit a somewhat dangerous one at times, but it represented an operational type now past and so was finally phased out of the School's inventory. The three Hawks were well and truly fitted into the flying syllabus and the School acquired a single-seat Jaguar GR 1 to replace the lost two-seater. Also on strength came the long-promised Lynx helicopter; unfortunately it was a DB aircraft (DB standing for Development Batch) and thus non-standard, giving a headache as regards servicing and spare parts. A twin-engined Wessex HU 5 replaced the aged Wessex HAS 3, again providing more flexibility in what could be done on the helicopter side. Six out of the fifteen students were British pilots, and one FTE, whilst from overseas a civilian test pilot came from Agusta, Mr R. Longobardi, with Captain J. W. Gisselman of the Swedish Air Force and Major G. P. Schittini of the Brazilian Air Force. No fewer than three of the overseas members were Australian, almost a take-over bid.

The Course became the biggest for some time, no fewer than eighteen souls, with yet another Air Force added to the list with the arrival of Captain M. Gonzalez of the Chilean Air Force. The Israelis, Canadians and USAF were back for more. In addition to the regulars, there was an Italian civilian pilot and a French Flight Test Engineer and yet another first, Mrs Valerie Shaw, a Boscombe Flight Test Engineer who became the first lady to undertake a Course at the school.

She had been working at Boscombe for the previous five years, having been promoted to Scientific Officer on gaining her degree and thus becoming eligible for the Course. It was recommended that she should apply for it and was at that stage in her career when it would benefit her most. She found she had a lot of gaps in her academic background and the ground school filled many of these in for her. Working in Performance Division she had

In a rare moment the Rotary Wing Course puts one of each type of helicopter in use by the School into the hover together in 1982. From front to rear they are Gazelle HT Mk 3 *XZ936*; Scout AH Mk 1 *XP849*; Lynx DB Mk 2 *XX510*; Wessex HU Mk 5 *XS509* and Sea King HAS Mk 1 *XV370*.

The most flexible of the helicopters that the School has had down the years has been the Westland Wessex in its various forms. *XS509* is one of the HU Mk 5s which joined in 1982.

already been doing some flying but mainly in the larger aircraft — Jetstream, Nimrod, etc — which she enjoyed. She said:

'I hadn't much experience in the small two-seater jet type aircraft and it took a couple of weeks to overcome my fear and relax and be able to do a useful job but now I thoroughly enjoy it. I just like flying and watching what is going on. The hard work comes at the end of the flight when you have to gather your data together, analyse it and sort out exactly what it means and write the report. You learn a lot as you go through the Course — I find I'm a lot quicker now.'

Asked if she found any problems being the only woman on the Course, she replied that the only problem was finding separate changing rooms for her to put on and take off her flying clothing. Otherwise she was treated in the same way as everybody else.

'It is a bit strange at first, until people

get to know you; but I think flying with the pilots has helped an awful lot because I think they gain more respect for you, rather than if you were just sitting on the ground doing the writing. The Course has been very hard work but I have a very understanding husband which has helped tremendously; otherwise I would not have been able to go through the Course.'

The Italians have been, down the years, one of the most regular supporters of ETPS. On the 1983 Course was Captain Andrea Canetto. He had flown mainly in the F-104 Starfighter during his ten years' service before coming to the School. The Italian Air Force had him at their test centre for six months, flying all different types of aircraft to prepare him before coming to England, and he went first to Leeming where he flew the Jet Provost and adapted himself to British R/T procedure and to the English language. It was a very rough period but useful, he thought, because when he came to the School he could understand nearly everything but still had trouble writing reports in English. For him the Course was so intense that at the time he found it difficult to appreciate its value. The Italian Air Force requirement, generally, is for one, two, or three test pilots a year and it is their practice to send one to ETPS, one to Edwards and one to EPNER or the US Navy. He was sent to Boscombe because there the most important thing is to succeed in the flying, whereas he was told that the major requirement of the USAF school at Edwards is the academics.

With regard to the flying, he said:

'My favourite aeroplane is the Lightning but unfortunately it is always broken. We don't have the opportunity to be in command in the Lightning because we have so few flights. One of the best things about this Course is that my airmanship has grown up in a great way because flying different types in the low weather minima in England is difficult for us, we are not used to such weather conditions.

'Now I am starting for my Preview and I have the Buccaneer, which is a very challenging aeroplane because it is a single stick aeroplane — there are no double controls, so my first flight will be solo and I think this is very representative of the job of a test pilot; you must fly an aeroplane that nobody has flown before and you must teach yourself without the help of anybody else. If you do something wrong you don't have the chance to do it again, so I am quite happy about the Buccaneer, but I am still very worried because I know it is very challenging. First of all I study the Pilots' Notes, all the limitations, the performance of the aeroplane, limits, warnings, and then I go to Honington

next week to fly the simulator to become familiar with the systems, to have a week of the ground school. I then fly to Cyprus where there is an Operational Conversion Unit. I will fly five hours in the aeroplane and then have to do all my tests in five hours. The American Navy pilot is with me and he will fly five hours, and in ten hours total flying we must finish all the tests to write the Preview. I think to fly the Buccaneer is very challenging because, being a single pilot aeroplane, you must take all your data measurements by yourself and pilot the aeroplane at the same time.'

The Course proceeded with no undue alarms and excursions and so the School completed forty years of training test pilots, forty years in which it pioneered the task and its accomplishment and, at the end of which, it has retained its pre-eminence in this field, having fought off all attempts by the financiers to draw its activities to a close. Its reputation now is world-wide and its expertise has been copied by a growing number of foreign services. In addition to the Indians, the South Africans have set up their own school (by an ex-graduate and staff member of ETPS, Duncan Cooke) and the Chinese are seeking advice from the School in order to set up their own establishment. Over these years, as well as supplying all the test flying needs for the British test flying scene, ETPS has graduated candidates from Canada, America, New Zealand, Holland, France, India, Italy, Sweden, Egypt, Switzerland, Malaysia, Chile, South Africa, China, Norway, Poland, Australia, Belgium, Greece, Germany, Thailand, Israel, Denmark and Brazil. Others are still to come.

So how does the Course look in the 1980s? Let Wing Commander Robin Hargreaves, CO up to 1984, describe it:

'The Course starts in February and finishes in December. It is divided into three terms with breaks for brief periods in between and, as far as the syllabus of training is concerned, the basic principle of that really hasn't changed for years. We start off with simple performance exercises. The students have just converted to quite a wide range of aircraft — we have six fixed-wing types and five helicopters — and that is already quite a handful for somebody who had, perhaps, only three types in his log book when he arrived. To get some consolidation on that range of aircraft we start them off on simple exercises which require them to fly the aircraft right in the middle of its flight envelope and just get quantitative data, which serves two purposes. First, it introduces them to data-gathering sorties, which require accurate flying

and accurate observations. Second, it gives them more flight time on the type; exercises such as pressure error corrections and static margins which don't require advanced handling techniques.

'That takes them through until about the middle of May and then the second term is June, July and August. It is chosen then because it is in that term that we do the more advanced handling exercises which require good weather — spinning, stalling and a new exercise which was introduced in 1977, when we started operating the Jaguars, which is a low-level systems assessment where they look at the Jaguar's navigation and weapon aiming system. That obviously requires good VMC weather, as does spinning, so in the middle term they are really getting into the area where they are looking

The School still carries on the traditions forged early in its history. Visits to Industry continue as witnessed by this Scottish-piper welcomed visit to Ferranti Limited at Turnhouse by the 1986 Course using the latest ETPS airliner, the BAC 111 Series 479F, *ZE432*.

at aircraft handling and developing their opinion as experts on what the handling characteristics of the aircraft are and what that means to the people who will be operating them.

'In the third term, which starts in September, they complete the advanced handling exercises with asymmetric which we do on the Andover or the Argosy. They then start to put everything together, everything they have learnt in separate packages, to do an overall evaluation of an aircraft. The first one they do is called the pilot's assessment and that's single flight evaluation of a simple aeroplane. For that you get a wide range of aircraft, still in service, of which the students can make sense in an hour/hour-and-a-half flying time. We have aircraft like the Devon, Heron, Beaver, Bulldog, Chipmunk, that sort of machine — and that's very useful because it lets us see how well the students have learnt, what they have learnt, in the individual exercises. It also leads them into the major exercise which is the graduation exercise on ETPS called the Preview.

'The Preview again is an overall evaluation of handling and performance. It is done on an aircraft that the students haven't flown before and it is done away from base — usually at the Operational Conversion Unit. It is done in teams of two or three and the team have ten hours' flying to share between them and in those ten hours they will have a look right across the aircraft's capabilities — its handling and performance, and its systems, and then write a massive report called the Preview Report. A presentation on their results is also given, and they have then graduated. It is a very packed syllabus and it is very difficult to introduce anything new into that syllabus without dropping something out. It is very difficult to drop anything out because it is all valuable stuff so there's an evolution of exercises as we get new aircraft — the exercises tend to become more complex but the basic requirement to look at longitudinal handling, lateral directional handling, asymmetric handling, performance, still remains, however modern and advanced the aircraft may be.

'What we have seen, slowly, is an increase in the content of system assessment exercises and the Jaguar on the fixed-wing side, and the Lynx and Sea King on the rotary-wing side, have allowed us to introduce a systems evaluation exercise. Of course, the employment of test pilots these days tends to be as much on the systems side as it does on the performance and handling side because there are fewer prototype aircraft around — aircraft tend to stay in service longer and in their time in service their systems, their avionics, tend to be updated once or maybe more, so that there is a lot of systems work there with aircraft modifications.

'Also, there is a lot of activity on the equipment side as new items of equipment are developed for aircraft — low light television, infra-red, radar sensors. There is an awful lot of work to be done in that area of systems assessment but it is not an easy one to teach because each system has to have specialised testing; so to teach it generally is difficult. You can lecture on systems on the ground, and we do a lot of that, you can assess systems that you actually possess, and this is why we use the Jaguar, Lynx and Sea King, but to teach systems testing right across the board is not possible, in fact. We concentrate on those areas where we have got hardware which we can assess and outside that we teach the elements of assessment which apply to any system. What we are interested in as pilots is the interface between the man and machine so we teach them how to assess the operation of the system, the ease of operating it, the acceptability of its controls, areas like that.'

Inevitably, although its members will deny it, the test flying fraternity is some-thing of an elite. The very work in which they engage requires men at the height of their professional abilities, and in the field of flying there can be few higher qualifications than that of being a graduate of the Empire Test Pilots' School. This is one of those British institutions, young in years but mature in experience, which stands at the forefront of British achievement and which will continue to retain this excellence into the 21st century.

Up-to-date hand over — In December 1988, Wing Commander John Bolton, on the right, hands over the command of the Empire Test Pilots' School to Wing Commander Martin Mayer, on the left. The latter is the first rotary wing graduate to return in command of the School.

CHAPTER 8
What They Flew

The School always had a miscellany of aircraft types and it is arguable that it has used more types than any other Royal Air Force unit. The Central Flying School might dispute this claim, but it is certain that no other unit has flown a wider diversity of types than has the Empire Test Pilots' School.

The composition of the School's fleet has always been a compromise, and always will be, between three variables. The first is what aircraft types are available, the second is what kinds of aircraft does the School need and the third, and dominant, variable is how much will the Ministry spend? For staff and Ministry alike it is always a question of balancing these three.

It is axiomatic that there shall be a variety of aircraft types in the fleet, otherwise much of the instruction will be unusable; although at times the Ministry men have seemed at a loss to understand this point and a comparison between the variety of the fleet in the 1940s and the types used now shows how heavy is the effect of the purse strings, though this can be obviated in other ways, as will be explained later.

When the first Course began it was an experimental effort in itself so its fleet was fragmentary, loaned from the Aeroplane & Armament Experimental Establishment to whom the aircraft returned at the end of the Course. Since then the staff have striven to maintain a balance of aircraft which will train the students for the likely tasks that they will have to face when they move out into their careers.

So, how would one set about assembling

an ideal fleet? The first factor to look into is the balance of classes of aircraft. The main types being tested today are the jet transports, the smaller piston and turboprop transports, the light piston and turboprop trainers, the fast jet fighter/strike aircraft and the helicopter, both heavy-lift maritime types and the small, agile, battlefield types. So there must be at least six types of aircraft in the fleet and, to give value for money, their selection must be such as to show, where possible, a wide variety of characteristics rather than simply being of a different class of aircraft. The next division is to find, in each class, standard production aircraft which are capable of a high utilisation and with a good spares backing because much of the Course each year is involved in teaching testing techniques and these can best be done on standard aircraft which are easy to maintain and cheap to operate. But, in addition to these, it is necessary to have some past experience of flying and of aircraft handling qualities so that a student will find himself facing situations quite outside his aviation experience and learn to adjust and cope with these.

Obviously, to cater for all these variations ideally would require an impossibly large fleet so, bearing in mind that Appendix 3 gives a complete fleet list of all known ETPS aircraft and that mention of many of the types has already been made in the foregoing chapters, let us review how the School met these problems down the years.

After the first experimental Course, the School built up a fleet of ten different standard types of aircraft in 1944 with three advanced trainers (two singles, one twin), three medium bombers (two four-engined, one twin), two light bomber types (one tricycle undercarriaged) and two single-engined fighter types. All these were standard operational types. The following year important additions were made; most significant being the urgent requirement for a jet fighter to be brought into the training loop. Two Meteors ful-filled this need and the students were able to learn all about the idiosyncrasies of early jet flight — the lag on opening throttles and the very high fuel burn. At the other end of the range, three biplanes were added including a Dominie. This latter was acquired partly for its ancient flying characteristics but more particularly as a suitable communications aircraft. Thereafter, at least one such suitable air-craft has been kept in the fleet to enable the School to accomplish its many flying visits.

This formed the basic composition for the next few years, although the actual types within these classes were changed. This was done with an eye on the types that were likely to be in test in the years ahead. For example, Tempests were added early on to the fleet as well as Fireflies, because these would be entering service, in different guises, for some years to come. At this time, too (1946), one or two aircraft were added to the fleet which would give some students problems in handling, such as the Seafire F 46. Also, the first glider — a Grunau Baby — arrived at this time, won from Teutonic sources, and started ETPS's long gliding association. This was the way the fleet looked whilst at Cranfield.

By the time it moved to Farnborough it had fourteen different types in the fleet maintaining the same balance as before, new types entering service being the Meteor F Mk 4 and the Sea Fury, as these types were just coming into front-line service with the RAF and RN respectively.

During the late 1940s the balance within the fighter side became more predominantly jet-orientated, whilst the DH Devon became the new communications aircraft. This lasted with the School for twenty years.

The early 1950s was the period when a whole new range of types was coming from the British aircraft industry, frontiers were being pushed back both in engine and airframe development and it was felt that ETPS needed more than simply production types in order to meet some of these challenges. So, types that were produced for Air Ministry contracts and failed to go into production began to filter through to ETPS. The first of these was the Avro Athena, a turboprop/piston trainer which served the School for a few years. But even with these types a problem showed itself which became exacerbated in the years ahead. This was the difficulty of obtaining spares for aircraft which had not had a long production run.

One of the needs of the tutors was to find aircraft which had dual controls for teaching students on classes of aircraft to which they were not used. This was particularly acute in the single-seat jet fighter area; to put a pilot of four-engined bombers or transports straight into a Meteor required quite a bit of faith and hope! So in 1952 a big step forward came with the arrival of the two-seat Meteor T 7s with which the tutors could take students aloft and demonstrate some of the peculiar characteristics of high and low-speed jet flight. This was reinforced the following year with the arrival of the Vampire T 11s, for the Vampire had different character-istics to the Meteor. Another standard type entering service at this time was the Hunting Provost T Mk 1 and this was a real gift to the School for, with such finely harmonised controls, so much could be demonstrated on the type, especially within the spinning regime.

The School was now in for a frustrating

few years for the new types entering the front-line were ahead of anything that the School could offer and so urgently were they needed in the squadrons that none could be spared for ETPS. Thus the Swift, Hunter and Canberra were all ahead of the School's capabilities. The first Hunter arrived in 1955, and the first Canberra in 1956. Both Canberra and Meteor were used to teach the asymmetric problems associated with twin-jet aircraft where the engines were almost mid-wingspan and as a result several fatalities occurred.

For the rest of the 1950s the fleet was consolidated, receiving newer versions of standard types and the occasional discarded prototype; almost always these were of limited value because the servicing headaches meant that they became hangar queens and were rarely serviceable to fly. In 1957, again somewhat after the Services' own experience, came the first helicopters, two Westland-Sikorsky Dragonflies, which served for six years with the School and provided the elements of helicopter test experience. In 1959 came what was to be one of the most significant of the School's types, the first two-seat Hunter. This enabled transonic characteristics to be demonstrated to students and, of course, was developed into the, by now famous, swept-wing spinning training which the School has developed to a fine art.

A significant step forward was made in 1962 when, for the first time, two aircraft were specifically bought (second-hand) for the School, rather than acquired from other organisations which had no further use for them. These two aircraft were Vickers Viscounts which performed many functions for the School. First of all, they provided suitable turboprop experience and training which, for students going on to the aero engine companies, was important. Up till now this had never really been covered satisfactorily, with the Apollo proving a maintenance nightmare and the Gannet's Double-Mamba

being somewhat unrepresentative. These Viscounts also gave the School its first experience of a modern airliner so that the training could be made more applicable to this type of aircraft. Lastly, the Viscounts provided the most magnificent airborne buses, enabling the School to make visits to other test establishments across the Atlantic as well as in Europe. They served ETPS well for ten years, eventually suffering from the Treasury axe.

The 1960s saw fairly rapid expansion in the helicopter field, to supplement the dated Dragonflies, but the School was beginning to hear a familiar moan from its students, principally the overseas ones: 'Why have you no supersonic aircraft in the fleet?' Of course, it was true, and it must have been very galling for, say, the American students, coming straight from an F-100 Super Sabre squadron where every flight was a supersonic one to a School to learn how to test future aircraft, only to find that it had nothing more than the transonic Hunter, and in order to get this supersonic you had to go into a steep dive! This problem was not fully solved until the School moved to Boscombe Down although the Ministry offered the School a sop in 1966 by giving them the second prototype two-seat Lightning, a very non-standard airframe. Coupled with the fact that Farnborough had no experience of Lightnings — nor ever had had, so there was no previous knowledge of this intricate type — the aircraft was not often serviceable for the next two years of the School's training programmes. Only when the School moved to Boscombe Down, where they had had wide experience of Lightnings and were still operating them, knowing this particular airframe of old, did this magnificent aircraft come into its own.

Another element came into the picture in the mid-1960s which hampered the School's efforts to build up an ideal training fleet. It was the beginning of the fashionable vogue in Governmental circles known as the Defence Cut Syndrome. Whenever a Government was getting short of ready money, which was depressingly often in those days of mounting inflation, the easiest way of recouping the balance was to have a defence cut for, unlike most other areas of operation, the Services could not go on strike if they disliked the idea. So from this time onwards the School has been under almost continuous pressure to reduce its fleet wherever possible.

One of the arguments put forward from time to time about the ETPS course was that students ought to be given the opportunity to fly types which were at the forefront of aeronautical development; the idea was a good one but it was largely impracticable from a cost point of view. However, occasionally prototypes which had finished their test programmes were drafted into the fleet. Examples were the Sea Venom, with blown flaps, and the Short S B5 but again the School was up against the old problem of a complete lack of spares backing and the need for a completely unrealistic amount of maintenance time to keep the aircraft flying. By their very nature such prototypes were used to doing a couple of flights and then going into the hangar for weeks or months of modifications. Such a practice could never fit into the hurried routine of ETPS and the system was dropped once the School left Farnborough.

Upon moving to Boscombe Down in 1968 the fleet was rationalised as follows: four Canberras, two Chipmunks, two Hunters, one DB Lightning, one Twin Pioneer and two Viscounts on the fixed-wing side and one Whirlwind and two Scouts on the rotary-wing side, together with three gliders. On order were two Beagle Bassets to fulfil the light communications rôle and to give yet another type for many of the exercises. It was with the second one of these that the next big fixed-wing development came.

With the fleet dwindling, and likely to dwindle even more in the future, what could be done to give the students that wide experience of aircraft handling characteristics so necessary for their complete training? The answer lay in making an aircraft fly in which the handling characteristics could be varied to show up bad or unpleasant reactions in certain parts of the flight envelope. Such a variable stability aircraft would be a valuable tool and this is what the second Basset became; details are given in Chapter Six. It meant that the School could in part cope with the narrowing of its fleet diversity so as to demonstrate, on this particular aircraft, a wide range of flight characteristics. This was also becoming important for, even if the fleet had been much wider, the standard of manufacture and testing in the 1970s and has since become so great that very few aircraft now come out of the factories with anything other than good handling qualities.

The urgent problem in the beginning of the 1970s was the rotary-wing course for no comprehensive course could be done simply on Whirlwinds and Scouts. This remained the difficulty until 1971 when the first Wessex came along but the major step forward was the arrival of a Sea King for the 1972 Course. Since then the School has had a fairly comprehensive selection of helicopters, enabling most of the different helicopter characteristics to be covered.

As is evident from the previous chapters, the testing sphere changed in content in the 1970s, with much greater emphasis on working out the huge diversity of black box operation on a much smaller number of new prototype aircraft. Thus, whilst the course at the School has to train students to do the basic handling testing, it also has to prepare them for the subtly different task of systems testing and in this way the School's task has become more diverse over the years, at the same time as the fleet has reduced in numbers and types. This latter problem has been met in two ways, catering for the two different areas in which such testing will be needed. One area is that of large, airline type operation in which there is a virtual revolution in the cockpit with whole new forms of flight instruments and methods of operation, as well as navigational and autopilot developments. The other is in the strike and battlefield area and here the developments are in systems which virtually do all the flying and fighting by computer. To some extent this also applies in the military helicopter field.

To cater for these areas the School has, during the last decade, re-equipped with types that can already demonstrate some of these devices but are also the type of airframes into which suitable equipment can be installed for systems testing training. The two transport aircraft on the fleet are an Andover, which has been with ETPS for twelve years, and a recent addition, a BAC One-Eleven airliner. These two are able to accommodate new equipment, instruments, etc, as well as cater for the transport requirements of the School. At the fast jet end of the range the School has, since 1976, been equipped with a varying number of Sepecat Jaguars. This type has an advanced navigational and weapons-aiming system, typical of the type of equipment now standard and enables the test-flying of this type of equipment to be realistically taught.

The other major fleet development that has taken place within the eighties has been the introduction of three British Aerospace Hawk T Mk 1s. This type, which is the RAF's standard advanced trainer, has the advantage of being easy to fly and maintain, with no spares backing problems and used to a high utilisation. The ETPS aircraft have been specially instrumented for the tasks which will largely consist of taking over from the Hunters, being used in the early part of the Course for such exercises as range and endurance and pressure error corrections, exercises which stem from the very beginnings of testing. They are then used to take the student up to more and more demanding exercises reaching the edge, and at times beyond, of the performance envelope of the aircraft. One of these three Hawks has just returned from a prolonged stay at Cranfield where it has been modified in the same way as the VSS Basset to become a variable stability demonstrator but in a much enhanced performance envelope including take-offs and landings. This aircraft will give the School a quantum jump in capabilities over the Basset and overcome the problems of a fleet which, for economic reasons, is a mere shadow of its former size.

However, this does not mean that a full range of testing exercises cannot be completed by the students. The fleet that is there enables the tutors to take the students well beyond any of their past experience; into areas of flight that they have been always taught to avoid in their past flying experience. For this the comprehensive Hunter upright and inverted spinning exercises are a good case in point, alongside the helicopter pilots' 'avoid curve' exercise which anyone outside the School would describe as dangerous; ETPS call it critical testing. So, despite the contraction of the ETPS fleet the School still provides a test training experience second to none in the world.

CHAPTER 9
The End Product

Having traced forty years of test pilot training, and realised that it is one of the more expensive of our defence commitments, the reader is entitled to ask: 'What was it all for? For forty years between ten and twenty pilots have completed the course and gained the coveted TP qualification, what good has it done for the nation(s) and for the pilots themselves?' So, it seems worthwhile tracing the paths that the average TP graduate made to find out the answers to these questions.

The Ministry of Defence has two main experimental establishments which require test pilots, and it is for the ongoing supply of competent pilots for these establishments that the ETPS courses are fundamentally set up. One is the Aeroplane & Armament Experimental Establishment at Boscombe Down, the other is the Royal Aircraft Establishment which has airfields at Farnborough, Bedford, Llanbedr and West Freugh. The former is concerned with testing aircraft for service in the Armed Forces, together with the armaments they carry; whilst the RAE is involved in more basic research into aerodynamics, weapons and electronics, together with the hundred and one items of equipment which make up the modern aircraft.

Each British Service pilot who graduates from ETPS normally undergoes one flying tour, of approximately 2½ years, with one or other of these establishments. Life becomes very different for him during such a tour — he has been used to working at very high pressure, studying, making reports, flying, very often at the edge of

his abilities, all being compacted into the smallest possible time scale in order to get through the course. However, when he gets to Farnborough or Bedford, or moves into different offices at Boscombe, he will find life very different.

The test scene inevitably involves much stopping and starting, changing and trying again. The first thing he will have to do is to convert to the aircraft on which his trial will take place, for most test pilots are allotted to specific trials. More often than not it will be an aircraft he has already flown but not necessarily for, at Farnborough or Bedford especially, many of the trials that are flown on equipment, or new techniques, are flown on old aircraft which make good equipment platforms, with room for all the test equipment which goes with the trials. For example, Farnborough, at the time of writing, is still flying a Vickers Varsity and de Havilland Comet C Mk 4, types which went out of service elsewhere years ago. This sometimes poses problems — for many years there was an old original Shackleton with a tailwheel undercarriage at Farnborough, and many of the test pilots going to Farnborough had little experience of such a configuration, particularly on a four-engined aircraft. Consequently, their first attempts at landing at Farnborough were always watched with amusement; in fact the aircraft became adorned with little 'Zebedee' stickers depicting the little coil-spring gentleman of 'Magic Roundabout' fame, for he most accurately summed up their performances! Incidentally, this aircraft is still to be seen, languishing with the ex-Strathallan collection, Zebedee stickers still on.

Having converted to the trials type the test pilot will then need to get to know the scientists in the department for which the trial is being carried out and to understand, as thoroughly as possible, what the trial is about, its limits and expectancy. Having done all this he will then be in a position to start the flying and this will depend on the availability of the equipment. Sometimes just one flight will reveal the need for modifications to the aircraft or the equipment which means waiting days, weeks or months. Then he will fly the same trial again and, very possibly, again and again and so on until the scientists get it right.

Such a flexible existence requires a certain phlegmatic patience that does not come to every pilot, a quality which is difficult to discover under the hard constraints of the ETPS course and which does not always mix with the other qualities of an individual who needs to be able to fly an aircraft to his own and the aircraft's limits. Many test pilots freely admit that it is not until towards the end of their first tour as a test pilot that they begin to understand and fall in with the way of life that is, of necessity, prevalent in test establishments, either from the irregularity of the flying or from the different work relations needed in a civilian scientific organisation.

Some of them then go for their next tour back into the operational side of their Service with a sense of relief, but very many of them become intrigued with the fascination of test flying, the quest for new knowledge, the spur to improve new equipment until it fulfils or exceeds specifications or the launching of some new concept or weapon at the very beginning of its developmental life. These are the pilots who will follow on with a second or third tour as test pilots and go on to make their careers in this sphere. For them the goals are likely to be to climb in the test establishments until they become Commanding Officer, Experimental Flying at Farnborough or Commandant at Boscombe Down, and these pilots give tremendous satisfaction to the individuals who teach them. Many of them will come back to the test scene after having spent some tours in the operational side of the Service. This is valuable, for the pilot takes his deeper knowledge of flying characteristics and abilities into the front line and then comes back to bring a sense of front line life and requirements into the much more academic atmosphere of the test establishments. Just such a one is the recent Commanding Officer at Farnborough, Group Captain Reg Hallam, who graduated on No 25 Course in 1966, then served as a test pilot at Farnborough and has now returned after several tours at the 'sharp end' with the air defence Phantom squadrons.

On the way up this test flying ladder other test pilots will find opportunities for their fulfilment outside their Service. The manufacturers are always on the lookout for promising additions to their test flying staffs and this will encourage many pilots to look for meaningful work outside the Service test flying area. This applies especially to the aircraft manufacturing companies for there can be little more satisfying to someone trained as a test pilot than to be given the developmental flying of a brand-new prototype, some gleaming new design that no one has ever flown before, and to carry out all the flying necessary to make it into a viable commercial success, an aircraft acceptable to the airworthiness authorities. Lieutenant Dave Eagles, RN, who graduated in 1963, eventually returned to the Fleet as Senior Pilot with No 809 Squadron flying Buccaneers from *HMS Hermes*, then made his name as Warton's Chief Test Pilot flying the Tornado. Others have found their way into all aspects of aviation life where they have taken the specific skills

A sight familiar to decades of ETPS students and tutors. A nice, curving, fighter-type approach to Boscombe Down's long east-west runway, with the westering sun behind on the last sortie of the day. In this case the view is from the tutor's seat of one of the School's Jaguars.

which ETPS has given them and applied them to the tasks in hand.

Almost all the American students go back to the various test establishments in the United States, either to the USAF's Edwards Air Force Base at Muroc or to the Naval Air Test Center at Patuxent River, homes of their own individual test pilots' schools. Thereafter their careers will follow a similar pattern to the British

graduates, some of them, such as Bill Pogue and Al Worden, becoming astronauts. The Frenchmen find service at the Centre d'Essais en Vol, which is their equivalent of Boscombe Down, and the occasional one is found on the staffs of companies such as Dassault-Breguet or Aérospatiale. This applies to most of the foreign nationals whose students are then employed either on their own test establishments or in their embryo or long-standing industries.

There are other spheres in which the test pilots serve. For example, the airworthiness authorities in this country, as part of the Air Registration Board, use ETPS graduates in the vital work of testing civil aircraft and assuring the nation that the aircraft are safe for public operation. It was ETPS graduates who did the considerable pioneer work in this field to certificate such an advanced public transport project as the BAC/Aérospatiale Concorde and the fact that these aircraft have been flying, in this advanced field, carrying fare-paying passengers for eleven years without hurting one of them is a tribute to the soundness of the testing given to these aircraft.

What, then, are the qualities required in the successful test pilot? This is not an easy question to answer for, to some extent, different types of test flying will appeal to different temperaments but there are certain qualities which are perhaps necessary for all of them. First of all, the test pilot must be physically fit. This is a *sine qua non*, for all forms of flying make physical demands and some forms of test flying will make extreme demands. Secondly, the test pilot must be emotionally stable and mature. This concerns not simply the stress of flying to the limits if necessary but more particularly the environment within which he will work. To cope with the frustrations and disappointments, the delays and reversals of plans demands maturity as well as the ability to cope with the people for whom he works, for the scientific mind and approach is very much diametrically opposed to the approach to life of the average military pilot. This brings an insidious, subtle form of stress, totally different to that of operational flying. Coupled with this goes the ability to get on well with all sorts of people, especially those with very different temperaments to himself — a man who does not suffer fools gladly will soon find himself unable to make his way as a good test pilot. To be able to see a problem from the other man's point of view is an almost essential asset in test flying work.

It goes without saying that the test pilot has to have above average flying ability but coupled with this is the need to have a good 'feel' for an aircraft; that is to be able, almost instinctively, to know what the aircraft is doing and how it is going to behave in the situations in which it is being flown. He has to be a confident pilot, not a timid one, but that confidence needs to be tempered with an ability to fear. The fearless pilot, contrary to what the entertainment media may have taught us about test flying in the past, is the pilot who will soon end up twenty feet below ground in the smoking ruins of his new prototype. This, however, is not all. He has to have a good academic brain so that he can grasp the theory behind the test he will undertake and be able to interpret what he is doing and what the test equipment is doing within the parameters of the actual test. Added to this, he needs to be able to write concise and accurate reports in order to bring back to the technicians and scientists the information needed to enable them to continue successful development of the aircraft, engine or equipment on test.

It is small wonder, then, that to be able to put the initials 'TP' after one's name is one of the most coveted awards in the field of military aviation, for it summarises a standard of flying excellence which is second to none. It is this standard which the Empire Test Pilots' School pioneered in 1943, before any other nation, and it is this standard that the School steadily maintains in the very different aviation environment of the 1980s. Long may it continue doing so.

CHAPTER 10
What of the Future?

After forty years of test pilot training and having been the original of all the test pilot schools, how does the future look for ETPS? This question was put to a recent Commanding Officer, Wing Commander John Bolton, and it is his view that there is an ongoing future for the School because it has already proved its worth and because the demand for a continual flow of test pilots stretches into the foreseeable future. Test pilots will always be needed and there is no short cut to producing a fully-fledged test pilot and guaranteeing the high standard which is part of ETPS tradition and which is the envy of so many air forces.

Much of the problem during its existence which has militated against the School has been the question of cost, but the School has learnt over the years that the answer is to be continually re-assessing its cost-effectiveness and working out methods of getting more and more out of its current resources. So, there is no apparent threat to the School from the financial aspect and a steady stream of students is anticipated, bearing in mind that a high proportion of students come from overseas. Whilst more overseas test pilot schools are being established, for most air forces this is simply not effective considering that their requirements are never more than one or two such test pilots per annum.

Changes in the curriculum and the fleet and equipment are expected to be more developmental than substantial. Over the four decades that ETPS has been operating it has been honing and refining its methods and equipment and knows very clearly the optimum levels both of equipment and of curriculum subjects so it is not anticipated that drastic changes will be necessary. Such changes in the latter, and in ground training equipment, will alter largely as a result of the changing emphases that will come from variations in the actual work of the test pilots after they have graduated. One such possibility is in the simulation field. At present more and more flying training is taking place on simulators and these are becoming ever more sophisticated. Already the Course involves some simulator assessment at the Royal Aircraft Establishment and this is likely to take on greater prominence.

With regard to the aircraft fleet, the future there looks more definite. The most important step is the return to Boscombe Down of the ASTRA Hawk, the one that has undergone modification at Cranfield as a variable-stability aircraft to take on, from the Basset, this rôle. This aircraft has a programmable HUD (head-up display) and digital fly-by-wire in the front controls so that digital problems can be taught and assessed in flight. It takes the variable-stability training into an entirely new realm because of the tremendous manoeuvre envelope of the Hawk; it is hoped that eventually the whole of that envelope will be usable for this purpose. This aircraft alone makes a tremendous difference to the possibilities available to the School. The Lightning has been one of the Achilles' heels of the School for its age meant that it had continuous servicing problems; this was replaced by a Tornado F 2 in 1988 and has given the School the advantage of having a swing-wing aircraft in its fleet, something that has been needed for some time. The Hunters, too, are getting long in the tooth and they will present a headache for replacement because no other aircraft has the spinning capabilities of this aircraft. The Hawk can go so far and it looks as though the School will have to settle for a modified spinning programme adapted to the Hawk. The Tucano is another aircraft being considered for the School, to replace the Jet Provost and perhaps to take on some of the Hunter's exercises as well. On the transport side ETPS has acquired a second-hand BAC One-Eleven and this should suffice, alongside the Andover, for many years to come. The rotary-wing side expects to replace its early prototype Sea King with an up-to-date version and to acquire a further Gazelle.

All down the years Britain has shown little incentive towards getting into the manned space field and indeed at the time of writing Britain's first spaceman, an ex-ETPS graduate, Squadron Leader Nigel Wood, has lost the opportunity to get into orbit. So it is not anticipated that the School will have much of a demand for teaching space pilots in the foreseeable future, although this may eventually change if the Hotol project were to move ahead.

So the Empire Test Pilots' School sees its half-century on the horizon and can reflect with pride on its achievements over four and a half decades. In 1943 it was an experimental project, something which no one had attempted to do before and so it established a pattern, principles and standards which formed a precedent for other nations which looked on, liked what they saw, and decided either to join in or to form their own Schools on very similar lines. Since then ETPS has continually refined its methods and reached towards ever high standards so that, even today, it stands supreme in the world. No higher piloting accolade can be given than to be a graduate of Britain's Empire Test Pilots' School. This reputation in itself must be a reward for all those devoted and far-sighted men who have striven to make the School what it is today. It is surely no hyperbole to say that by setting rigorous standards and teachable methods for the art of test flying the School has revolutionised the post-war test flying scene; this in itself is an immense achievement in the world of aviation.

Appendix One
COMMANDING OFFICERS

1943-1944 Wg. Cdr. S. Wroath, AFC
1944-1945 Gp. Capt. J. F. X. McKenna, AFC
1945-1947 Gp. Capt. H. J. Wilson, AFC
1947-1948 Gp. Capt. S. R. Ubee, AFC
1949-1950 Gp. Capt. L. S. Snaith, AFC
1950-1953 Gp. Capt. A. E. Clouston, DSO, DFC, AFC
1953-1957 Gp. Capt. S. Wroath, CBE, AFC
1957-1960 Gp. Capt. R. E. Burns, CBE, AFC
1960-1961 Capt. K. R. Hickson, AFC
1962-1965 Gp. Capt. R. A. Watts, AFC
1966-1969 Gp. Capt. W. J. P. Straker, AFC

1969-1970 Capt. P. C. S. Chilton, AFC
1971-1973 Gp. Capt. D. P. Hall, AFC
1973-1975 Gp. Capt. H. A. Merriman, CBE, AFC
1975-1976 Gp. Capt. M. K. Adams, AFC
1976-1977 Wg. Cdr. J. A. Robinson, AFC
1977-1980 Wg. Cdr. J. E. Watts-Phillips
1981-1985 Wg. Cdr. R. S. Hargreaves, BSc(Eng), MRAeS
1985-1988 Wg. Cdr. J. W. A. Bolton, BSc, MRAeS
1988-   Wg. Cdr. W. L. M. Mayer, AFC, MRAeS

N.B. the Commanding Officer's Post was entitled as under:
1943-1976 Commandant
1976-1980 Chief Instructor
1980-   Officer Commanding

Appendix Two
ETPS BASES

5/43 to 10/45 Boscombe Down
10/45 to 8/47 Cranfield

8/47 to 1/68 Farnborough
1/68 to   Boscombe Down

Appendix Three
AIRCRAFT USED

Airspeed A.S.10. Oxford I (6/43-5/53) — AS504, HN272, HN581, HN782, LX198, MP449, NM247, NM805, PG935, PG936, PH122, PH509, RR328, RR345.
Airspeed A.S.10. Oxford II (5/44-6/45) — T1257, AB658, AB705
Armstrong Whitworth A.W.55. Apollo (9/54-9/55) — VX224 '15'
Armstrong Whitworth A.W.660 Argosy C.1 (4/71-5/77) — XN814, XR105
Auster AOP.5 (9/47-7/50) — TJ524, TW460
Auster AOP.6 (11/48-6/53) — VF627

Avro 652A Anson C.19 (12/46-3/51) — VP509
Avro 652A Anson T.21 (3/49-11/51) — VV319
Avro 683 Lancaster I (5/44- /46) — R5612, R5842, HK710, ME830, PP789
Avro 683 Lancaster II (4/45-11/45) — ED491, EE108
Avro 694 Lincoln B.2 (10/46-9/57) — RF354, RF416 '15', RF456 '15', RF528, RF534, RF535 '16', RF538
Avro 696 Shackleton MR.2 (11/60-3/62) — WG557
Avro 701 Athena T.2 (8/50-4/52) — VR568, VR578, VW890, VW893

Avro 707B (/56- /57) — VX790 '19'

B.A.C. One-Eleven Srs.479FU (3/84- date) — ZE432

B.A.C. Jet Provost T.5 (7/75-date) — XS230

Beagle Basset CC.1 (3/68-date) — XS742, XS743

Blackburn Beverley C.1 (/57- /58) — XB259 '17'

Boulton Paul P.108 Balliol T.1 (7/52-5/53) — VL892

Boulton Paul P.108 Balliol T.2 (1/52-7/53) — VR592, VR597, VR605, VW899

Bristol 152 Beaufort II (6/43-10/43) — AW343

Bristol 171 Sycamore 3 (7/54-3/58) — XH682

de Havilland D.H.82A. Tiger Moth II (4/45-10/46) — T6831, T6859

de Havilland D.H.89A. Dominie I (9/45-5/53) — HG715

de Havilland D.H.98A. Mosquito II (3/44-9/44) — W4090

de Havilland D.H.98. Mosquito III (4/47-4/52) — HJ888, HJ898 '23', LR567, RR284, TW101, VP342

de Havilland D.H.98. Mosquito IV (2/44- /44) — DZ590

de Havilland D.H.98. Mosquito VI (2/45-11/45) — HX855, RF644, RF648, RS505

de Havilland D.H.98. Mosquito B.20 (2/44- /44) — KB328

de Havilland D.H.98. Mosquito B.25 (3/45-6/45) — KB552

de Havilland D.H.98. Mosquito B.35 (9/47-6/49) — RS719, RS720, RS721

de Havilland D.H.100. Vampire F.1 (6/46-4/50) — TG338, TG345, TG368, TG386, TG387, TG388, VF313

de Havilland D.H.100. Vampire F.3 (12/49-3/51) — VT818, VT857

de Havilland D.H.100. Vampire FB.5 (3/49-7/53) — VV618, VV620, VV672, VV679, VZ350, VZ835, WG801

de Havilland D.H.104. Devon C.1 (12/51-11/67) — VP979 '4', VP980 '1', WF984 '4', XA879 '2'

de Havilland D.H.112. Venom FB.1 (10/52-7/53) — WE282

de Havilland D.H.112. Sea Venom FAW.21 (6/58-11/58) — WM574 '18'

de Havilland D.H.115. Vampire T.11 (6/58-5/62) — WZ451 '16', WZ475 '17'

de Havilland D.H.C1. Chipmunk T.10 (6/58-2/75) — WB549 '7', WD321 '3', WD334 '3', WD374 '3'

Douglas Boston IIIA (2/45- /46) — BZ252, BZ346

Douglas Dakota III (11/45-10/46) — TS431

English Electric Canberra B.2 (8/59-10/69) — WE121 '19', WH715 '27', WH854 '30', WH876, WJ730, '18', WJ994 '19', WK129

English Electric Canberra T.4 (6/58-1/82) — WH844, WJ865, WJ867 '10'

English Electric Lightning T.4 (5/66-11/75) — XL629 '23'

English Electric Lightning T.5 (7/75-8/87) — XS422, XS457

Fairey Swordfish II (3/45-10/45) — HS642

Fairey Firefly I (8/46-6/52) — Z1953, DK429, PP639, PP641, PP648

Fairey Gannet T.2 (9/55-6/62) — XA515 '24', XG873 '27'

Fieseler Storch (6/50- /50) — VP546

Gloster G.41A Meteor F.1 (4/45- /46) — EE213

Gloster G.41C/E Meteor F.3 (7/45-6/49) — EE348, EE350, EE397, EE398

Gloster G.41F Meteor F.4 (8/46-4/52) — EE454, EE491, EE568, VT338, VS302, VW303

Gloster G.43 Meteor T.7 (5/58-11/66) — WA638 '8', WF822 '11', WH231 '8', WL377, WL488 '11'

Gloster G.41K Meteor F.8 (1/52-9/55) — VZ438, WF752, WH498, WK660 '9'

Gloster G.47 Meteor NF.11 (6/58-3/60) — WD765 '5', WD769 '1', WD797 '9'

Gloster G.47 Meteor NF.14 (8/59-6/62) — WS793 '5', WS845 '6'

Grunau Baby (/46-?) — LN:ST

Handley Page H.P.57. Halifax I (5/43- 8/43) — L9520

Handley Page H.P.57. Halifax II (7/43- 11/43) — R9436

Handley Page H.P.61. Halifax III (?) — LV904

Handley Page H.P.57. Halifax V (5/44- 10/44) — DK236, LL272, LL397

Handley Page H.P.68. Hastings C.1 (5/53-5/62) — TG501 '17'

Hawker Hurricane I (5/43-6/43) — L2006

Hawker Hurricane IIA (6/43-9/43) — Z2399

Hawker Hurricane IIC (8/43-9/44) LD264, LF418, LF422

Hawker Tempest II (8/45-11/49) — MW767, MW775, MW791, MW813, PR622, PR918, PR919

Hawker Tempest V (3/45-10/45) — JN732, JN739, JN770

Hawker Tempest VI (/46-?) — NX121, NX243

Hawker Sea Fury FB.10 (3/48-7/53) — SR661, TF895, TF897, TF922

Hawker Sea Fury FB.11 (5/52-7/53) — WE728

Hawker Sea Fury T.20 (2/52-6/53) — VX818

Hawker Sea Hawk F.1/FGA.4 (/53-10/59) — WF196 '27', WV910 '20'

Hawker Hunter F.1 (9/55-9/59) — WT572 '26', WT621 '23', WT624 '26'

Hawker Hunter F.4 (7/59-3/62) — WV374, XF940 '25', XF969 '26', XF970 '25'

Hawker Hunter F.6 (1/65-5/82) — WW592 '26', XE587, XF375 '6'

Hawker Hunter T.7 (5/60-date) — WV253 '24', XJ615 '23', XL564, XL579 '25', XL612, XL616

Hawker Siddeley Andover C.1 (9/75- date) — XS606

Hawker Siddeley Hawk T.1 (5/81-date) — XX313, XX341, XX342, XX343

Hunting-Percival Provost T.1 (4/53-9/67) — WV420 '21', WV425 '21', WV551, WV577 '22', XF685 '20'

Hunting-Percival Pembroke C.1 (/55- 5/58) — WV698, WV710 '25'

Lockheed Hudson III (4/45- /46) — T9418, V9222

Miles M.9 Master I (/43- /44) — T8886

Miles M.16 Mentor I (/44-6/44) — L4393

Miles M.19 Master II (1/44-5/44) — DM345, DM427, EM389

Miles M.27 Master III (5/43-10/43) — W8537

North American Harvard IIB (5/44-3/51) — FS718, FS902, FX229, FX281, FX337, FX354, FX365 '1', FX371, FX373, FX402, KF177, KF314, KF427 '3', KF562

North American Mitchell II (8/43-10/44) — FL192, FL215, FL688, FV984

Panavia Tornado F.2 (11/87-date) — ZD900, ZD935

Percival P.31A Proctor IV (6/43- /43) — MX451

Scottish Aviation Twin Pioneer (4/65-2/75) — XT610 '22'

Sepecat Jaguar GR.1 (1/82-date) — XX119

Sepecat Jaguar T.2 (7/76-date) — XX145, XX830, XX835, XX841, XX844, XX915, XX916

Schleicher Ka6OR (7/69-4/75) — XW640

Short S.B.5. (12/65-11/67) — WG768 '28'

Siebel Si 204 (6/46- /47) —

Slingsby Sedbergh TX.1 (3/68-4/75) — WB920

Slingsby Olympia (6/47-11/69) — VV400 '60', VV401

Slingsby Sky (8/52-1/75) — XA876 '59'

Supermarine Spitfire VB (2/44-10/44) — W3112, W3322

Supermarine Spitfire VC (2/44- /44) — MA648

Supermarine Spitfire VII (2/44- /44) — AB450

Supermarine Spitfire VIII (6/44-9/44) — LV674

Supermarine Spitfire IX (2/44- /47) — BS352, JL165, ML174, NH174, NH194, NH478, SL663

Supermarine Spitfire XII (2/44- /44) — MB878

Supermarine Spitfire XIII (2/44-11/44) — W3112

Supermarine Spitfire F.21 (4/45- /46) — LA192

Supermarine Spitfire F.22 (5/52-1/53) — PK495

Supermarine Seafire F.46 (/46-4/48) — LA546, LA549, LA557, LA558

Supermarine Seafire F.47 (4/48-6/49) — PS944, PS945

Supermarine Swift F.7 (8/60-9/61) — XF113 '19'

Supermarine Scimitar F.1 (/63-/7/64) — XD216 '22'

Vickers 417 Wellington III (2/44-10/45) — X3549, X3788, BK450

Vickers 498 Viking IA/C.2 (3/50-9/52) — VL231 '22', VW215

Vickers 651 Valetta C.1 (10/48-9/55) — VL266, VL268, WD171 '24'

Vickers 664 Valetta T.3 (9/55- /59) — WJ463 '21'

Vickers 668 Varsity T.1 (3/52-9/61) — VX828 '12', VX835, WF381 '14', WF387 '15', WJ937 '12', WL681 '11'

Vickers 744/745 Viscount (1/62-5/72) — XR801, XR802

Westland WS.51 Dragonfly HR.1/HR.3 (6/58-2/65) — VX595 '29', WG662 '28'

Westland WS.55 Whirlwind HAS. 7/HAR.3 (12/62-3/71) — XK907 '9', XJ759 '4'

Westland WS.55/3 Whirlwind HAR.10 (7/68-2/77) — XJ398, XJ409

Westland P.531 Scout AH.1 (1/65-date) — XP165 '5', XP849, XR436 '4'

Westland Wessex HU.5 (9/77-10/85) — XS509

Westland Sea King HAS.1, HC.4 (12/71-date) — XV370, XV371, ZG829

Westland/Aerospatiale Gazelle HT.3 (5/78-date) — XZ936, XZ939

Westland/Aerospatiale Puma HC.1 (12/72-12/75) — XW233

Westland WG.13 Lynx AH.1/AH.7 (2/82-date) — XX510, XZ179, ZD560

Appendix Four
COURSE LISTS

Legend: AC = Sir Alan Cobham Trophy; D = Dunlop Trophy; E = Edwards Award; H = Hunter Trophy; M = McKenna Trophy; P = Patuxent Shield; W = Westland Trophy.

No. 1 Course 1943-44

G. R. Callingham, RN
A. K. Cook, RAF
G. V. Fryer, RAF
M. W. Hartford, RAF
H. G. Hazelden, RAF

R. V. Muspratt, RAF
J. C. Nelson, RAF
K. J. Sewell, RAF (killed in flying accident, March 1955 — Pembroke)
G. P. L. Shea-Simonds, RNVR
P. H. A. Simmonds, RAF (killed in flying accident, March 1947 — Mosquito)

J. C. S. Turner, RAF (killed in flying accident, September 1945 — Vampire)

P. F. Webster, RAF (killed in flying accident — Firefly)

D. D. Weightman, RAF (killed in flying accident, October 1948 — Brigand)

No. 2 Course 1944-1945

J. Adam, SAAF

E. L. Baudoux, RCAF

N. J. Bonnar, RAF (killed in flying accident on course)

L. R. Brady, RAAF (killed in flying accident on course)

P. C. Chen, Chinese AF

E. E. Collins, RAF

S. E. Esler, RAF (killed in flying accident, 30 September 1949)

E. G. Franklin, RAF

A. P. Goodfellow, RNVR

C. V. Haines, RAF

R. E. Havercroft, RAF

M. J. Lithgow, RN (killed in flying accident, 22 October 1963 — BAC 1-11)

C. T. Loh, Chinese AF

J. A. Lyon, RNVR

R. M. Mace, RCAF

J. R. Muehlberg, USAAF

J. A. C. Northway, Bristol Aeroplane Co. (killed in flying accident, May 1949 — Bristol Freighter)

J. H. Orrell, A. V. Roe & Co.

W. B. Price-Owen, RAF

E. Sandberg, R. Norwegian AF

R. L. Smith, RAF

H. Snyder, USAAF (killed in flying accident, 1955)

I. Somerville, RCAF

F. Squire, RAF

J. B. Starky, RNZAF

R. M. Trousdale, RAF (killed in flying accident, 1947 — Mosquito)

K. H. F. Waller

J. Zurakowski, R. Polish AF

No. 3 Course 1945

F. R. Bird, RAF

J. S. Booth, RAF (killed in flying accident, 1958)

J. Bridge, RNVR (killed in flying accident, 1947 — Meteor)

B. E. Bullivant, AFRAES RNVR

H. V. B. Burgerhout, Netherlands Navy

R. E. Clear, Airspeed Co.

E. Coton, RAF

D. R. Cuming, RAAF (M)

M. W. Davenport, USN

J. J. Davidson, USN

R. S. Easby, RAF

E. B. Gale, RCAF (killed in flying accident, 1946 — Mustang)

A. Glover, RAF

J. D. E. Guignard, French AF

J. F. Handasyde, RAAF

R. C. Howeing, USAAF

J. O. Lancaster, RAF

E. W. Leach, USAF (killed in flying accident, July 1945 — Oxford)

J. M. N. Legrand, Belgian AF

J. G. Mann, RAF

G. C. B. McClure, RAF

A. R. Moore, RAF

S. F. Orr, RNVR

C. F. Phripp, RCAF

T. A. G. Randell, RNVR

W. G. M. Sanders, Handley Page Co.

E. J. Saunderson, RAF

J. C. K. Sutton, RAF

H. N. Sweetman, RNZAF

L. P. Twiss, RNVR

D. J. B. Wilson, RAF (killed in flying accident, August 1947 — Tudor)

No. 4 Course 1946

P. P. C. Barthropp, RAF

M. E. Blackstone, RAF (killed in flying accident, March 1951 — Hastings)

K. A. Butler, RAF (killed in flying accident, February 1950 — Spitfire)

P. R. Cope, RAF

I. D. Crozier, RAF

D. P. Davies, RNVR

H. J. Dodson, RAF

N. F. Duke, RAF

W. H. Else, RAF

P. G. Evans, RAF (killed in flying accident, September 1948 — Hastings)

R. S. Flight, RAF

P. R. Fowler, RAF

W. D. K. Franklin, RAF

P. J. Garner, RAF (killed in flying accident, 1947 — Wyvern)

G. E. C. Genders, DFM, RAF (killed in flying accident, 1950 — DH 108)

K. C. M. Giddings, RAF

H. C. N. Goodhart, RN

J. G. Haigh, RAF

E. L. Heath, RAF

K. R. Hickson, RN

R. C. Hockey, RAF

D. A. C. Hunt, RAF

D. H. G. Ince, RAF

P. G. Lawrence, RN (killed in flying accident, 1953 — Javelin)

K. A. Major, RAF (killed in flying accident, 1949 — SRA1 Flying Boat)

R. B. Mancus, RNVR
A. E. Marriott, RAF
R. F. Martin, RAF
E. F. S. May, RAF
T. F. Neil, RAF
J. F. Rankin, RCNVR
D. A. Taylor, RAF
P. S. Wilson, RN

No. 5 Course 1946-1947

C. M. Adams, RAF
G. C. Baldwin, RN
B. Bastable, RAF (killed in flying accident, May 1949 — Marathon)
M. E. Blackstone, RAF
D. J. P. Broomfield, RAF (killed in flying accident, August 1951 — HP 88)
C. B. Brown, RAF
F. E. Clark, RAF
P. R. Cope, RAF
I. D. Crozier, RAF
H. J. Dobson, RAF
J. F. Fewell, RCAF
W. M. Foster, RCAF (M)
N. F. Duke, RAF
W. H. Else, RAF
R. B. Giblin, USN
K. C. M. Giddings, RAF
H. S. Hwang, Chinese AF
L. G. Kiggell, RN
T. J. A. King-Joyce, RN (killed in flying accident — Attacker)
H. Kontolefas, Royal Hellenic AF
S. C. Lu, Chinese Af
D. J. Masters
R. F. Martin, RAF
J. C. Miles, DAP Australia
T. F. Neil, RAF
K. V. Robertson, RAAF
W. P. Smith, USN (killed in flying accident, 1950 — Cutlass)
G. Sonderman, R Netherlands AF (killed in flying accident, October 1955 — Fokker S14)
E. N. M. Sparks, RAF
J. J. Stone, USAF

No. 6 Course 1947

G. Banner, RAF
T. W. Brooke-Smith
C. L. Brooks, RAF
A. E. Callard, RAF
V. B. Carson, RCAF
G. J. Chandler, RAF
R. M. Crosley, RN
L. C. E. De Vigne, RAF
R. L. Duncan, RAF
D. A. Dunlop, RAF
V. R. L. Evans, RAF

N. F. Harrison, SAAF
G. F. Hawkes, RN
H. E. Hoerner, USN
G. W. Johnson, RAF
W. F. Krantz, USN
A. C. Lindsay, RN (killed in flying accident, 1951 — Attacker)
L. S. Lumsdain, RAF (killed in flying accident, 1966 — CL41 Tutor)
I. M. MacLachlan, RN (killed serving in Korea)
D. G. McCall, RAF (killed in flying accident, 1949 — Sealand)
S. McCreigh, RAF
J. S. R. Muller-Rowland, RAF (killed in flying accident, 1950 — DH 108)
R. H. Reynolds, RN
P. Richmond, RN
W. H. Scott, RAAF
L. W. F. Stark, RAF
J. R. Stoop, RAF
A. Tooth, RAF (killed in flying accident)
R. A. Watts, RAF
R. W. Whittome, RAF (M) (killed in flying accident, 1948 — Spitfire)
D. J. Williams, CDF(A)
R. G. Woodman, RAF

No. 7 Course 1948

M. R. Alston, RAF (killed in flying accident, May 1956 — Canberra)
A. Ashworth, RAF
J. S. Bailey, RN
A. C. Capper, RAF
P. C. S. Chilton, RN
J. Elliot, RN (M)
W. H. Fearon, RCN
B. L. Grubaugh, USAF (killed in flying accident, June 1958 — F100)
A. E. Gunn, RAF
P. A. Hartman, RCAF
S. J. Hubbard, RAF
I. N. M. MacDonald, RAF
R. B. Meyersburg, USMC
D. W. Morgan, RN
W. J. O. Morrison, RAF
D. G. Parker, RN
P. L. Parrott, RAF
E. J. Roberts, RAF (killed in flying accident, 1959 — Gnat)
C. L. T. Sawle, RCAF (killed in flying accident, September 1949 — Meteor)
C. K. Saxelby, RAF
W. J. Sheehan, RAF
R. Smyth, RAF
D. G. Tayler

No. 8 Course 1949

B. G. Aston, RAF

A. W. Bedford
R. Bradwell, RAF
D. W. Butler, RAF
F. Cawood, RN (killed in flying accident — Sea Venom)
C. G. Clark, RAF (killed in flying accident, November 1952 — Venom)
R. W. F. Cleever, RAF (killed in flying accident, October 1953 — Vampire)
S. Das, RIAF (killed in flying accident — HF 24)
J. M. Davis, USAF (killed in flying accident, April 1953)
R. V. Ecclestone, RAF (killed in flying accident, July 1954 — Victor)
E. D. Glaser, RAF
M. W. Grierson-Jackson, RAF
J. G. Harrison, RAF
J. W. L. Innes, RAF
G. K. N. Lloyd, RAF
R. M. Orr-Ewing, RN (killed in flying accident, 1950 — Attacker)
J. H. Phillips, CDF(A)
C. E. Price, RN
B. Radley, RAF
J. Robertson, RN (killed in flying accident)
J. A. Rowlands, RAAF
J. G. Smith, USN (M)
R. L. Suri, RIAF
E. A. Tennant, RAF
B. Warren, RCAF (killed in flying accident, April 1951 — Canuk)
G. T. Weems, USN (killed in flying accident, January 1951)
D. White, RAF
A. D. Woodcock, RAF

No. 9 Course 1950

D. E. Biden, CDF(A)
J. E. Burton
J. Castagnola, RAF
R. A. Clarke, USN
D. W. Colquhoun, RAF (killed in flying accident, 1953 — Sea Hawk)
W. W. Elliott, USAF
H. N. Garbett, RAF
W. R. Gellatly, RAF
D. K. Hanson, RN (killed in flying accident, 1951 — Wyvern)
M. T. Harding-Rolls, RAF
G. A. Heck CDF(A) (M)
R. M. Herrington, USAF
C. S. Hunton, RAF
T. G. Innes, RN
C. H. Macfie, RAF
D. J. Murphy, RAF (killed in flying accident, 22 June 1954 — Sea Fury)
S. B. Oliver, RN
W. N. Plews, RN (killed in flying accident, 1950 — Lincoln)

W. J. Runciman, RAF (killed in flying accident — Sea Mew)
J. R. Saunders, RAF
J. C. Sloan, RCN
C. W. Stark, RAAF (killed in flying accident on course — Vampire)
W. J. P. Straker, RAF
F. C. Turner, USN
L. M. Whittington, RAF

No. 10 Course 1951

P. C. Bowry, RAF
R. B. Connell, RAF (killed in flying accident, 12 July 1951 — Sea Fury)
K. W. Dalton-Golding, RAF (killed in flying accident — Canberra)
R. E. Evans, USAF (killed in flying accident 1958)
A. E. Facer, RN (killed in flying accident, 1952 — Sea Venom)
J. S. Fallon, USAF (killed in flying accident, 1952)
P. G. Fisher, RAAF (killed in flying accident, 1952 — Dakota)
L. E. Flint, USN
B. J. L. Greenland, RAF
L. P. Griffith, RAF
R. C. R. Hallett, RN
T. S. Harris, RAF
J. K. Hough, RAF (M) (killed in flying accident, 1953 — Sycamore)
N. J. M. Kearney, RAF
P. M. Lamb, RN
N. E. D. Lewis, RAF (killed in flying accident, 1953 — Swift)
P. E. Payne, USN
O. B. Phillip, CDF(A)
W. K. Potocki, RAF
W. H. Sear, RN
B. Singh, RIAF
J. A. Sowrey, RAF
P. D. Thorne, RAF
R. L. Topp, RAF
J. P. Tyszko, RAF (killed in flying accident in Sweden, January 1965 — Cessna)

No. 11 Course 1952

K. M. Ashley, RAF (killed in flying accident, 1974)
H. J. Cobb, RAF
J. F. Cotton, USAF
J. M. Crowley, RAF
V. H. Fourie, RAF
T. P. Frost, RAF
B. K. Ghosh, RIAF
R. J. D. Glendinning, RN
A. Harper, RAF
G. M. Hart, USN
C. A. C. Jonas, RAF

R. Kinder, RAF
B. J. S. Knight, RAF
W. J. Laidler, RAF
C. McK. Little, RN
M. Marcovitch, RAAF (killed in flying accident on course — Valetta)
C. N. C. Mitchell, RAF
W. Musgrave, RAF
W. Noble, RN
A. G. H. Perkins, RN
R. J. Ross, RAF (M) (killed in flying accident, 1954 — Javelin)
A. I. R. Shaw, RN
W. S. Stewart, III, USN
E. M. Stringer, USAF
J. W. Sutherland, RAF
R. E. Tickner, RAF
W. A. Tofts, RN
C. A. Tomlinson, RAF
P. W. Varley, RAF
I. B. Webster, RAF
L. H. Wilkinson, RAF (killed in flying accident on course — Valetta)
A. H. Wittridge, RAF
J. F. Woodman, RCAF

No. 12 Course 1953

P. P. Baker, RAF
P. Barlow, RN (killed in flying accident, 1965)
S. A. Bernardini, Italian AF
T. A. Berry, RAF
P. W. Bryce, USAF (killed in flying accident, 1955 — F89)
J. T. Checketts, RN
A. D. Dick, RAF
D. D. Engen, USN
A. L. B. Faucett, RAF (killed in flying accident, 1954 — KZ 10)
G. R. K. Fletcher, RAF
B. O. J. Fryklund, R Swedish AF (M) (killed in flying accident, 1954 — Lansen)
R. A. Harvey, RAF
J. C. Henry, CDF(A)
J. Hourlier, French AF
J. P. Jacobs Jr, USAF
A. C. Koplewski, USN (killed in flying accident, 1953 — Wyvern)
W. D. Lang, RN
B. W. Mead, RCN
R. V. Morris, Fairey Aviation Co.
J. R. Overbury, RN (killed in flying accident, 1960 — Jet Provost)
J. D. Price, RAF
T. A. Rickell, RN (killed in flying accident, 1955 — Supermarine 525)
E. C. Rigg, RAF
E. J. Shaw, RAF

No. 13 Course 1954

M. H. Beeching, RAF
R. Bignamini, Italian AF (M) (killed in flying accident)
A. L. Blackman, RAF
F. W. Botts Jr, USN
O. Brage-Anderssen, Royal Norw. AF
J. G. Burns, RAF
N. N. Ducker, RN
R. M. Fernbaugh, USAF
J. Franchi, French AF
W. R. Hart, RN
J. J. Harvie, RCN
W. J. P. Heynen, R Neth. AF
G. R. Higgs, RN
V. J. Hill, RAAF (M)
H. G. Julian, RN
S. R. Kersey, RCAF
I. C. Kincheloe Jr, USAF (killed in flying accident, 1958 — F104)
E. V. Mellor, RAF
G. H. Moreau, RAF
J. A. Moyles, RCAF
J. L. Price, RAF
R. T. Robinson, RAF
L. P. Stuart-Smith, RAF (killed in flying accident, 1959 — Tudor)
B. Sukhanusasna, R Thai AF
P. P. Trevisan, Italian AF
R. Walker, RAF
D. J. Whitehead, RN
C. K. Williamson, RAF

No. 14 Course 1955

P. J. Allavie, USAF
S. W. Bainbridge, RAF
P. J. Bardon, RAF
D. Le R. Bird, RAF
E. D. Blake, RAF
R. W. Bray, RAF
C. M. Bruce, RAF
R. Carlquist, USN
A. M. Christie, RAF
L. A. Coe, RAF (killed in flying accident, 1956 — Canberra)
M. Colagiovani, Italian AF
M. J. Cottee, RAAF
F. A. Cousins, RAAF
M. W. Cross, RAF
S. H. R. L. D'Arcy, RAF
H. J. Davies, RAF
P. S. Davis, RN
D. L. P. Delavergne, French N
D. F. Fieldhouse, RN (killed in flying accident, January 1963)
G. Franchini, Italian AF
W. Gadzos, (Canadian civilian)

S. W. Grossmith, RCN
O. J. Hawkins, RAF
F. Hefford, RN
W. D. M. Miller
R. E. Moore, USN (M)
K. J. Murray, RAAF
D. P. Norman, RN
L. J. O. Prudence, RAF
D. F. Robbins, RN
E. N. Ronaasen, CDF(A)
D. K. Roxberry, RAF
R. J. Spiers, RAF
E. F. H. Staaf, R Swed. AF (killed in flying
    accident, 1956 — Lancaster)
E. A. Strutt, RCAF
J. W. Waldie, RCAF
J. Walhout, R. Neth. AF
F. Zaher, Egyptian AF (killed in flying accident,
    1955 — Hunter)

No. 15 Course 1956

B. A. Ashley, RAF
J. R. Ayres, CDF(A)
K. Bhargava, Indian AF
G. S. Burdick, USN
G. C. Cairns, RAF
D. B. Cartlidge, RAF
E. Cauda, Italian AF
G. W. F. Charles, RAF
J. G. Cruse, RAF
J. P. F. Desalis, RAF
B. W. Dodd, RAF
D. E. Farr II, USAF
H. O. Field, RAF
A. E. Fox, CDF(S)
J. D. Gibson, RAF
R. R. Green, RAAF
J. A. Hablot, French N
J. E. Hanna, CDF(A)
M. J. Hedges, RN
J. S. Humphreys, RN (M)
D. A. Kribs Jr, USN
L. Lenoble, R. Belgian AF
D. A. Lethem, RAF
A. McVitie, RAF
A. L. Nelson, RCAF
B. J. Noble, RAF
P. I. Normand, RN
M. Quarantelli, Italian AF
P. B. Reynolds, RN
G. B. Stockman, RAF (killed in flying accident,
    1959 — Victor)
A. Sudhakaran, Indian AF (killed in flying
    accident, 1960)
G. A. V. Tullsson, R. Swed. AF
D. J. Woodman, RAAF

No. 16 Course 1957

E. R. Anson, RN
H. M. Archer, RAF
A. Bowman, RCAF
P. M. L. Brey, Fokker Aircraft
F. T. Brown, USN
W. D. Cam, RN
D. G. Cameron, RAAF
J. L. J. Cannac, French AF
I. M. Chopra, Indian AF
R. J. Cockburn, RCAF
D. A. Cooper, RAF
P. K. Dey, Indian AF
T. C. Evans, RN (M)
M. S. Goodfellow, RAF
T. E. M. Kirby, RN
R. N. Law, RAAF
R. S. May, RAF (killed in flying accident, 1958
    — Javelin)
J. G. McCormick, USAF
M. A. McNeile, RAF
H. A. Merriman, RAF
R. J. Morgan, RAF (killed in flying accident,
    1959 — Victor)
J. A. Neilson, RN
A. C. O'Neal, USN
L. B. Pollock, RCAF
I. A. G. Svensson, RAF
D. H. Tate, CDF(S)
L. I. A. Taylor, RAF
G. C. Wilkinson, RAF

No. 17 Course 1958

H. Andonian, USAF
R. E. Aslund, USN
J. L. Barnes, RAF
J. D. Blackwood, USN
O. Brown, RN (killed in flying accident, 1961 —
    Buccaneer)
B. Brownlow, RAF
L. G. Cockerill, RAF
J. D. Cook, RAF
J. A. Fryer, RAF
C. V. Gole, Indian AF (M)
S. W. Holmes, RAF
J. W. Hough, RCAF
J. S. Hurll, RAF (killed at ETPS, 29 June 1965 —
    Dragonfly)
C. B. Lewis, RAF
J. Lewis-Lloyd, RAF
J. M. Lowe, Indian AF (killed in flying accident,
    1969 — Gnat)
P. Millett, RN
U. Musicanti, Italian AF
J. D. Penrose, RAF
A. W. Pickering, RAF
W. R. Shackleton, RN (killed in flying accident
    — Meteor)

J. I. Thomson, RAAF
R. A. Whyte, RAF (E)
J. Wilkinson, RAF

No. 18 Course 1959

P. J. Barber, RN
J. R. Blatch, RAF
S. G. Corps, RAF
N. G. Emslie, RAF (killed in flying accident on course — Varsity)
J. R. Green, RAF (killed in flying accident, 1963 — SC 1)
D. P. Hall, RAF
J. M. Henderson, RAF (E)
J. G. F. Hewitt, RAF
B. M. Holland, RN
J. R. Lees, USAF
R. A. Lees, RAF
M. Marchesi, Italian AF
J. K. Mohlah, Indian AF (killed in flying accident — HR 24)
L. R. Moxam, RAF
W. A. Newton, RN
R. W. Paige, USN (killed in flying accident, 19 December 1961)
D. Parratt, RAF
L. B. Persson, R Swed. AF
H. R. Radford, RAF (M)
L. J. Roberts, RAF
T. H. Sheppard, RAF
J. T. Spafford, RN
D. Stinton, RAF
G. W. Talbot, RAAF
J. J. Taylor, USN (killed in action, S. E. Asia, December 1965)
M. W. Tilak, Indian AF
R. A. White, CDF(A)

No. 19 Course 1960

J. R. Aitken, RAF
W. A. Anderson, RAF
J. D. Barwell, RAF
N. T. Bennett, RN
R. De V. Boult, RAF
G. T. Cannon, RAF
J. A. Carrodus, RN
W. A. Cato, USAF
J. Cockrane, RAF
B. H. Collings, RAAF
B. Davies, RN
E. J. Hogan Jr, USN
L. N. Hoover, USN (M)
I. H. Keppie, RAF (H)
P. J. Lovick, RN (E)
G. M. Morrison, RAF
J. J. Parker, RAF
S. S. Rajan, Indian AF

R. D. Sahni, Indian AF
D. M. A. Samuels, RAF
G. M. Turner, RAF
J. W. Waterton, RAF
B. Wood, RAF (killed in helicopter accident in Canada, 196?)
D. B. Wright, RAF

No. 20 Course 1961

W. A. J. Bale, RN
R. Brading, RAF
R. E. Brinckman, USAF (missing in Vietnam, 1966)
H. J. Campbell Jr, USN
T. E. B. Chambers, RAF (killed in flying accident, 1982 — Harvard)
F. D. Cretney, RAF
J. B. Cross, RN
G. G. Davies, RAF
H. W. A. Deacon, RN (H)
B. K. Dhiman, Indian AF
J. A. Dietz, RAAF
R. A. E. Dunn, RAF (E)
P. J. Farris, RAF
R. G. Gallinger, RCAF
B. Hopkins, RAF
J. E. C. Mayes, RAF (P)
E. Nappi, Italian AF
C. T. B. Peile, RAF
W. J. Peters, USN
P. E. Reeve, RAFC
C. Rustin, RAF (M)
P. Singh, Indian AF
E. C. Turner, RAF

No. 21 Course 1962

R. L. Beeson, RAF (killed in flying accident Boscombe Down, May 1968 — Hunter T7)
P. J. R. R. Brittan, RN
B. Carroll, RAF (P)
A. Fisher, RAF
R. G. Green, RAAF
J. S. Hardiman, RAF
J. K. Isherwood
W. C. Mackison, RAF (killed in flying accident West Freugh, June 1966 — Buccaneer)
J. I. Meeker, USAF (M) (killed while doing Reserve training for National Air Guard, 1965 — F100)
R. L. Merritt, USN
C. R. Newnes, RN
D. Oldham, RAF (killed in flying accident on course, 25 October 1962)
E. N. Palmer, RN
P. M. Ramachandran, Indian AF (E)
J. A. Robinson, RAF
D. C. Scouller, RAF
D. D. Timm, USN

G. Varin, French AF (H)
A. J. W. Whitaker, RAF
J. L. Williams, RN
M. R. Williams, RAF
N. M. Williams, RAF (killed in flying accident,
  13 December 1977 — Heinkel)
N. R. Williams, RAF
K. Yadav, Indian AF

No. 22 Course and No. 1 Rotary Wing Course 1963

M. K. Adams, RAF (M)
P. Ashoka, Indian AF (E and H)
J. R. Ayres, RAF
J. C. K. Baerselman, RAF
R. P. Bentham, RCAF
B. J. Bullivant, RN
G. S. Cryer, RN
J. D. Davis, RAF
D. E. Deadman, RAF
J. S. Disher, USN
J. D. Eagles, RN
J. F. Farley, RAF (P)
R. T. Foster, RAF
E. D. Frith, RAF
T. E. Gill, RAF
M. C. Ginn, RAF (W)
J. R. Harper, RAF
M. B. Hawkins, RAF (killed in flying accident
  Canada, 1974)
J. P. R. Jackson, AAC
A. Matte, Italian AF (killed in flying accident,
  April 1964)
J. I. Miller, RAF
R. F. Mundy, RAF (E)
D. J. Parry, RAF
W. R. Pogue, USAF
J. P. Skyrud, USN

No. 23 Course and No. 2 Rotary Wing Course 1964

F. Amaldi, Italian AF
P. E. H. Banfield, RN (E)
O. Benato, Italian AF (killed in flying accident,
  1967)
M. Bigois, French AF (killed in flying accident
  on course, 24 June 1964)
M. W. Buss, USAF (H)
D. L. Bywayter, RAF (P)
T. P. Cripps, RAF
B. L. Gartner, CDF(A)
B. S. Grieve, RAF
A. J. Hawkes, RAF
G. H. Herbert, CDF(A)
M. Hope, RN (W)
M. A. Loves, RAAF
K. L. Narayanan, Indian AF
P. A. Polski, USN

T. E. Riddihough, RAF (M)
H. W. J. Rigg, RAF
R. T. Slatter, RN
J. F. Strong, RAF
J. E. Watts- Phillips, RAF
R. Woodhouse, RAF
A. M. Worden, USAF (P)

No. 24 Fixed Wing Course and No. 3 Rotary Wing Course 1965

G. D. Andrews, RAF
W. L. Corley, US Army
A. S. Cottingham, RAF
W. Davies, USN (E)
J. T. Egginton, RAF
E. K. Enevoldson, USAF
L. Fe D'Ostiani, Italian AF (P)
S. C. Fisher RAAF (H and M)
C. J. Horscroft, RN
B. D. Jayal, Indian AF
L. G. Locke, RN (W)
T. Mason, RAF
O. P. Mathur, Indian AF (killed in flying
  accident on course, 11 March 1965)
K. K. Saini, Indian AF
J. W. Spencer, USAF

No. 25 Fixed Wing and No. 4 Rotary Wing Course 1966

D. Berger, USAF
H. J. W. Bothma, SAAF
G. E. Bridges, RAF
C. R. Bubeck, USN
P. R. Carter, AAC
J. H. Cox, RAAF (W)
W. J. Dennis, CDF(A)
D. W. Gates, RAF (H)
R. P. Hallam, RAF
P. J. G. Harper, RN (E)
A. C. E. Holbourn, RAF
A. P. S. Jones, RAF
H. B. Lake, RAF
T. L. Lecky-Thompson, RAF
J. L. Légaré, French AF
J. T. S. Lewis, RAF (P)
R. Mombelli, Italian AF
G. F. Moore, RAAF
W. E. Newman, USN
S. G. Pearce, RAF (H) (killed in flying accident,
  10 August 1976 — Nomad)
A. K. Sapre, Indian AF (killed in flying accident
  — HF 24)
K. Singh, Indian AF
R. O. Sutton, RN
A. Van Der Schraaf
D. Wachtel, (W. German Civilian)
D. T. Ward, USAF (M)
G. C. Williams, RAF
N. R. J. Wingate, RAF (H)

No. 26 Fixed Wing and No. 5 Rotary Wing Course 1967

C. P. Allen, RN
K. P. Clarke, RAF
I. G. Conradi, RAF
A. D. A. Cooke, RAF (E)
B. M. E. Forward, RAF
L. V. P. Galvin, CDF (A) (W)
D. H. Goodsir, RAF
B. J. Graf, RAF (P)
B. I. L. Hamilton, RAF
W. D. Mauschild, USAF
K. N. J. Hawes, RAF
A. H. Hopkins, RAAF
W. M. Howard, RN
F. F. Hughes Jr, USN
W. V. Klein, USN (H and M)
A. S. Lamba, Indian AF
G. J. McIntosh, RAF (H)
J. M. Morgan, RAF
L. Nielson
R. C. O'Day, RAN (H)
K. F. Robertson, RAF
I. S. Sandhu, Indian AF
B. J. Tonkinson, RAF
J. P. Van Acker Le Lec, French AF
G. Warren, RAF

No. 27 Fixed Wing Course and No. 6 Rotary Wing Course 1968

M. M. Charles, RAF
A. A. Clark, RAF (M)
J. G. Depui, French AF (killed in flying accident on course, 1 October 1968 — Canberra)
D. J. G. Foster, RAF
H. E. Frick, RAF
R. S. Graustein, USN (posted missing over Hanoi, 21 December 1972)
E. M. Horne, RN
S. Kereliuk, CDF(A)
D. P. M. Nixon, RAF
G. A. Peterkin, RAAF (H)
M. F. L. Purse, RN (W)
R. V. Richardson, RAAF (H)
A. J. Sheppard, RAF
B. W. Skillicorn, RAF
B. P. L. Stokes, RAF
D. J. Thigpen
C. A. Wheal, RN (P)
H. D. Williams, AAC (E)

No. 28 Fixed Wing Course and No. 7 Rotary Wing Course 1969

J. D. Blake, RAF (P)
V. F. Champion, French N (E)
F. Colussi, Italian AF
L. Diloreto, USN

K. J. Doyle, RAAF
T. K. Gilmore, RAF
K. Koglin, (W. German Civilian) (H)
M. Laughlin, RAF
R. G. Ledwidge, RAF (M)
W. S. Lowe, RAN
W. L. M. Mayer, RAF (W)
C. J. H. Richardson, RAF
R. H. G. Statham, RAF
I. W. Strachan, RAF
J. White, RN
B. A. Wilson, RAAF (H)
U. Yaari, Israeli AF (H)

No. 29 Fixed Wing Course and No. 8 Rotary Wing Course 1970

A. R. Baker, (Civil Aviation Branch, Canada) (M)
R. G. Davis, RAF (H)
C. J. Furse, RAAF (P)
W. G. Gevaux, RAF
M. A. Hindley, RAF
B. Le Cornec, French AF (H)
D. F. Moffatt, RAF (W)
B. Peaty, RAF
R. K. Pottratz, USN (P)
H. F. Rammensee, (W. German Civilian) (H)
P. A. Reddel, RAAF
K. E. Reid, AAC
M. H. B. Snelling, RAF
W. Spychiger, Swiss AF (E)
R. J. Trease, RAAF

No. 30 Fixed Wing Course and No. 9 Rotary Wing Course 1971

J. Ambler, RAF
R. D. Brown, RAF
C. Calzoni, Italian AF
E. Coeuret, French AF (H)
P. G. Dickens, RAAF
N. C. Haag, R. Swedish N (E)
M. Kenworthy, RN
S. Krishnaswamy, Indian AF
K. H. Lang, (W. German Civilian) (P)
L. R. Millar, RAF
K. N. Rauch, USN
D. C. Reid, RAF
J. Rudin, RAF
J. R. Sadler, RAF
P. A. Sedgwick, RAF (H and M)
N. G. Warner, RAF
J. R. A. Whitney, RAF (W)

No. 31 Fixed Wing Course and No. 10 Rotary Wing Course 1972

T. R. Adcock, RAF
J. C. Boitier, French AF

P. G. Buckland, RAF (H)
S. M. STC Collins, RAF (W)
R. A. Dean, SAAF
W. C. Durham, USN
T. L. Farquharsen, RAAF (M)
J. H. Fawcett, RAF (P)
P. A. Freize, RAF
P. Gordon-Johnson, RAF
C. W. Hague, Rn (H)
R. A. Howard, RAAF
D. P. Robson, RAAF
A. Rom, Israeli AF (E)
P. Smith, RAF
G. Sprenger, (W. German Civilian) (H)
D. A. Stangroom, RAF

No. 32 Fixed Wing Course and No 11 Rotary Wing Course 1973

R. H. Beazley, RAF (H)
H. C. Bradford, RAAF
R. D. Cole, RAF
C. Colombo, Italian AF
H. J. Deus
K. B. Engelsman, RAN (W)
J. H. Finney, USN (H)
D. H. Jackson, RAF (P)
V. P. Kala, Indian AF
J. C. Lagardere, French AF
J. A. P. Marais
D. J. Marpole, AAC
P. G. Nicholson, RAAF (M)
R. Pengelly, RAF (killed in flying accident, June 1979 — Tornado)
R. H. N. Rhodes, RAF
D. Seeck, German Navy
P. C. Tait, RAF (E)

No. 33 Fixed Wing Course, No. 12 Rotary Wing Course and No. 1 Flight Test Engineer Course 1974

M. Barral, French AF
D. H. Beswick, RN (H)
M. Betts, RAF (H and W)
H. Betz, (W. German Civilian)
J. L. Bishop, RAF
J. W. A. Bolton, RAF (M)
J. L. P. Denning, (FTE) (D)
A. M. Eldred, (FTE)
G. E. Evangelisti, AF (P)
I. E. Frost, RAF (E)
J. W. Kindler, RAAF
A. A. McDicken, RAF
H. J. Nelson, RAF
J. M. O'Dwyer, RAF (killed in flying accident, 1975 — Meteor)
J. Rush, RN
W. Steward, AAC

J. W. Thorpe, RAF (AC)
J. R. Watkins, USN
D. Yadav, Indian AF (killed in flying accident)

No. 34 Fixed Wing Course, No. 13 Rotary Wing Course and No. 2 Flight Test Engineer Course 1975

B. Bellucci, Italian AF (E)
M. C. Brooke, RAF
T. Creed, RAF (W)
G. A. Ellis, RAF (P)
M. J. Hayler, RAAF
S. Hjort, R. Danish AF (H)
R. J. Humphries, (FTE) (D)
U. Kerkhoff, (W. German Civilian)
E. Kus, (W. German Civilian)
G. Le Bretton, French AF
V. C. Lockwood, RAF
D. Morgan (FTE) (killed in flying accident)
T. A. Morgenfield, USN (M)
S. C. Rastogi, Italian AF
D. McD. Ross, RAF
R. W. Searle, RAF
N. A. Sellers, (FTE)
S. C. Thornewill, RN
R. Tierney, RAF
P. K. Yadav, Indian AF
C. J. Yeo, RAF (H and AC)

No. 35 Fixed Wing Course, No. 14 Rotary Wing Course and No. 3 Flight Test Engineer Course 1976

J. H. Allen, RAF (W)
R. McP. Auld, CAF
A. V. Awalegaonkar, Indian AF (H)
D. W. Blackhall, (FTE)
I. L. Gonsal, RAAF
P. Habert, French Navy (M)
M. C. Hagen, RN (AC, P and H)
K. A. Hartley, RAF
Y. Ilan, Israeli AF (FTE)
R. F. Job, (FTE)
T. R. A. Jones, RAAF
I. Laestadious, R. Swedish Army
F. C. Lentz, USN (E and H)
J. C. Martin, (FTE) (D)
T. F. K. Miller, RAF
G. Puglisi, Italian AF (killed in flying accident on course — Argosy)
J. Rochfort, RAF
A. Shaked, Israeli AF (H) (killed in flying accident — Dornier Do28)
A. A. Shakir, (FTE)
P. C. D. Vowles, RN
W. A. Wainwright, RAF

No. 36 Fixed Wing Course, No. 15 Rotary Wing Course and No. 4 Flight Test Engineer Course 1977

K. N. Atkin, RN
J. T. Baker, R Netherlands AF
W. E. Beaty, USN
P. J. Bennett, RAF
R. A. Cowpe, RAF (P)
P. J. Dunford, (FTE)
J. W. Foley, RAAF (E)
R. V. Frederiksen, RN
A. Frediani, Italian AF (AC and H)
A. J. Hayhurst, AAC
R. D. Kobierski, CAF
M. Maharik, Israeli AF (FTE) (D)
N. Pande, Indian AF
T. D. Ralston, (S. African Civilian) (M and W)
C. F. Roberts, RAF (H)
P. L. Sadler, RAAF
M. R. Swales, RN
J. R. Wiseman, (FTE)

No. 37 Fixed Wing Course, No. 16 Rotary Wing Course and No. 5 Flight Test Engineer Course 1978

N. D. Arnall-Culliford, RN (E)
J. Brown, RAF
P. P. R. Baudry, French AF (P)
D. Benedetti, Italian AF (D)
R. Burton, (FTE)
D. J. Chapman, RN (W)
R. H. Calwer, German Navy
L. T. Dufraimont, CAF
R. B. Haack, RAAF
G. R. J. Holder, RE
G. Marani, Italian AF (M)
M. J. McCulley, USN
A. F. Philip, RAF
A. Ridzwan Salleh, R. Malaysian AF
G. J. Tomlinson, RAF (AC, H and M)
C. D. Upadhyay, Indian AF
H. P. Weger, (W. German Civilian)

No. 38 Fixed Wing Course, No. 17 Rotary Wing Course and No. 6 Flight Test Engineer Course 1979

A. Bescombes, French AF
T. H. Brown, RAF (AC)
C. J. Chadwick, RN
S. C. Coyle, Canadian AF
D. Finney, USN
A. R. Foster, RAF (P and H)
P. Kemsley, (FTE) (H)
D. Koren, Israeli AF
Lim Tow Leang, R. Malaysian AF
R. J. North, RAF
A. Noy, Israeli AF (W)
A. M. Oliver, (FTE) (D)

O. S. Panato, Italian AF
D. Reeh, RAF (H and M)
W. H. Spears, RAAF
K. C. Spreadborough, (FTE)
U. Vecchi, Italian AF (E)

No. 39 Fixed Wing Course, No. 18 Rotary Wing Course and No. 7 Flight Test Engineer Course 1980

T. N. Allen, RAF
R. Badham, (FTE) (D)
B. S. Baldwin, RN
A. F. Banfield, RAF
L. Benard, French AF
J. N. Blackburn, RAAF (H, M and P)
S. P. Dennis, (FTE)
R. Giola, Italian AF (killed in flying accident, 1981 — MB 326)
P. G. Habel, USN (H)
H. Hickle, German AF (E)
D. Jesse, (FTE)
M. F. Lake, RN
T. J. McCormick, RAAF (AC)
J. E. M. Mustard, RAF (W)
R. Peart, RAF

No. 40 Fixed Wing Course, No. 19 Rotary Wing Course and No. 8 Flight Test Engineer Course 1981

Alwi, R. Malaysian AF
J. J. Barnett, RAF (AC and M)
T. Brown, USN
J. P. Haignere, French AF (P)
L. B. Hammond Jr, USAF
W. Havenstein, German Navy
P. I. M. Rainey, RN
G. C. Rulfs, RAAF
P. Scoponi, Italian AF
N. Talbot, AAC (E)
E. R. A. Van Kleef
A. Webb, AAC
I. Young, RAF (W)
A. J. Houghton, (FTE) (D)

No. 41 Fixed Wing Course, No. 20 Rotary Wing Course and No. 9 Flight Test Engineer Course 1982

H. R. Cowan, RN
J. W. Gisselman, Swedish AF
D. A. Z. James, RAF (AC)
R. D. Jenkins, RAAF
K. Jones, (D)
K. W. Jurd, RAAF
R. Longobardi, (Italian Civilian) (W)
D. E. McKay, CAF
B. W. Moss, USN
T. P. Newman, RAF (H)

G. P. Schittini, Brazilian AF
M. Tognini, French AF (P and H)
A. Warner, AAC
C. J. M. Wilcock, RAF
S. J. Wood, RAF (E)
R. N. Woodward, RAAF (M)

No. 42 Fixed Wing Course, No. 21 Rotary Wing Course and No. 10 Flight Test Engineer Course 1983

A. Canetto, Italian AF
D. C. Dunn, CAF
P. D. Dye, RAF (AC and M)
A. Bar-Eyal, Israeli AF
B. Van Eyle, RAAF (P)
S. J. Fielder, RAAF
B. M. H. Foron, RAF
B. R. Fouques, (FTE) (D)
F. Frisi
C. R. Glaeser, USAF
J. A. Goddard, RAF (E)
M. Gonzalez, Chilean AF
A. M. S. Kahlon, Indian AF
A. D. Mechling, USN
C. W. Pittaway, RN
V. H. Shaw, (FTE)
R. Tuxford, RAF
T. J. Wood, RAF (W)

No. 43 Fixed Wing Course, No. 22 Rotary Wing Course and No. 11 Flight Test Engineer Course 1984

J. D. Avery, RAF
P. Bertrand, French AF
D. W. Carpenter, RAF (Retd)
R. L. Foulkes, RAF
M. Joel, RAAF
N. Kidd, RN
J. B. A. Lacharite, CAF
S. G. Mould, RAF (Retd)
H. Northey, RAF
J. O'Halloran, RAAF
M. R. Ottone, Italian AF
J. R. Pope, RAF
R. P. Radley, RAF
B. Roorda, RNLAF
J. J. Tartaglione, USN
S. R. Thomas, RN (Retd)

No. 44 Fixed Wing Course and No. 23 Rotary Wing Course 1985

S. J. E. Aubert, French AF
N. G. Coulson, RAAF
T. L. Evans, RAF
H. G. Fehl, German AF
A. J. Howden, RN

T. Koelzer, USN
Koh Joon Teh, R Singapore AF
J. S. Ludford, RAF
R. H. Meiklejohn, CAF
S. J. Moore, RNZAF
D. R. Southwood, RAF
R. J. Tydeman, RAF
G. Yannai, Israeli AF
M. Zuliani, Italian AF

No. 45 Fixed Wing Course, No. 24 Rotary Wing Course and No. 12 Flight Test Engineer Course 1986

A. R. Bodiam, RAF
U. Bredemeier, German AF
G. A. W. Connolly, RAF
E. Davelaar, RNIAF
M. C. Edwards, RAF
E. W. H. Fitzpatrick, AAC
P. Glinfuang, RTAF
C. S. Handley
M. J. Keane, USAF (deceased)
T. F. Klassen, CAF
N. G. Lindorff, RAAF
S. G. Lloyd-Morrison, RAF
S. Lockert, RNoAF
R. J. Ormshaw, RN
R. H. Rutherford, USN
G. Salvestroni, ItAF
J. Turner, RAF
A. Vallee, FAF
P. G. Whitfield, AAC

No. 46 Fixed Wing Course and No. 25 Rotary Wing Course 1987

M. L. Bathrick, USN
M. H. de Courcier, RAF
P. Deleume, FAF
A. F. E. di Pietro, RAN
S. L. Goodier, RAAF
S. N. Hargreaves, RN
C. Lelaie, Aerospatiale
D. C. Maclaine, AAC
G. J. McClymont, RAF
C. C. Morris, RAAF
B. Schafer, MBB
W. Schirdewahn, GAF
H. Siffl, GAF
D. A. Simpson, RAF
M. Talmor, Israeli AF
C. Worning, RDAF

No. 47 Fixed Wing Course and No. 26 Rotary Wing Course 1988

M. Angerer, German Navy
A. M. J. Bray, RAF
C. D. Brown, RN

I. C. Burrett, RAF
M. Cheli, IAF
F. A. S. Courreges, FAF
W. Druck, GAA
S. Dunkle, USN
De M. S. Eitel, Brazilian AF
C. Jensen, Swedish AF
M. C. Kirkpatrick, CAF
O. Knoller, Israeli AF
C. Nicollier, ESA
C. J. Van de Cappelle, RNLAF
P. J. Wright, AAC

No. 48 Fixed Wing Course, No. 27 Rotary Wing Course and No. 13 Flight Test Engineer Course 1989

A. C. Berryman, RN
V. Bertozzi, IAF
D. Best, RAF
I. R. Burton, AAC
P. J. Collins, RAF
A. Cooke, RAF
K. J. Emerson, RAF
K. D. Flade, GAF
G. Gelee, FAF
J. Holden, CAF
D. J. Hunter, USAF
S. Johns, MOD (PE)

M. G. Jones, Aust AA
J. W. Knowles, USN
I. W. McClelland, RAF
P. J. Richie, AAC
P. Serra, IAF
R. Trigg, MOD (PE)
R. Zehavi, Israeli AF

No. 49 Fixed Wing Course, No. 28 Rotary Wing Course and No. 14 Flight Test Engineer Course 1990

M. N. Bowman, RAF
V. Casagrande, IAF
P. D. Q. Chapman, RN
N. S. Dawson, RAF
E. Lupinacci, IAF
K. H. Mai, GAF
A. J. Morris, RAAF
W. E. Ovel, RAF
P. C. Richings, RN
S. Schreiber, USN
A. P. Sharpe, AAC
J. G. G. Simard, CAF
S. E. Smith, RAF
A. Spence, RAF
A. Strachan, RAF
J. D. Warren, RAF
A. Young, RAF

Index